INQUIRY INTO SCIENCE

RICHARD SCHLEGEL is Professor of Physics at Michigan State University, where his teaching and research interests are directed toward theoretical physics and questions in the philosophy of science. During his period of appointment at Michigan State, Dr. Schlegel has spent sabbatical years at Cambridge University in England and has taught courses in physics and the philosophy of science at the University of California at Berkeley, the University of Texas at Arlington, and the Center for the Philosophy of Science at the University of Minnesota. In addition, he has contributed articles to numerous scientific journals, among them *American Journal of Physics* and *Nature*.

THE SCIENCE STUDY SERIES offers to students and to the general public the writing of distinguished authors on the most stirring and fundamental topics of science, from the smallest-known particles to the whole universe. Some of the books tell of the role of science in the world of man, his technology and civilization. Others are biographical in nature, telling the fascinating stories of the great discoverers and their discoveries. All the authors have been selected both for expertness in the fields they discuss and for ability to communicate their special knowledge and their own views in an interesting way. The primary purpose of these books is to provide a survey within the grasp of the young student or the layman. Many of the books, it is hoped, will encourage the reader to make his own investigations of natural phenomena.

The Series, which now offers topics in all the sciences and their applications, had its beginning in a project to revise the secondary schools' physics curriculum. At the Massachusetts Institute of Technology during 1956, a group of physicists, high school teachers, journalists, apparatus designers, film producers, and other specialists organized the Physical Science Study Committee, now operating as a part of Educational Services Incorporated, Watertown, Massachusetts. They pooled their knowledge and experience toward the design and creation of aids to the learning of physics. Initially their effort was supported by the National Science Foundation, which has continued to aid the program. The Ford Foundation, the Fund for the Advancement of Education, and the Alfred P. Sloan Foundation have also given support. The Committee has created a textbook, an extensive film series, a laboratory guide, especially designed apparatus, and a teachers' source book.

INQUIRY INTO SCIENCE
ITS DOMAIN AND LIMITS

RICHARD SCHLEGEL

ILLUSTRATIONS BY AL NAGY

SCIENCE
STUDY
SERIES

PUBLISHED BY ANCHOR BOOKS

DOUBLEDAY & COMPANY, INC.

GARDEN CITY, NEW YORK

1972

CONTENTS

LIST OF PHOTOGRAPHS

PREFACE

I have attempted in this book to present in a popular form some of the major points that can be made about the extent and the limits of science. Much of my treatment is similar to that given in parts of my book, *Completeness in Science,* published in 1967 by Appleton-Century-Crofts, New York, and the reader may be referred to that work for more technical discussions and for literature references. But even though the line of argument and the conclusions that I come to are the same as in the larger work, I hope that this book may have an approach and spirit of its own. In particular, I have laid somewhat greater emphasis on the relations of science to other kinds of human inquiry.

The book was first published, in 1969, in a German translation with the title *Steckbrief der Wissenschaft,* by Deutsche Verlags-Anstalt, Stuttgart. The text of the present American edition is virtually the same as that of the English-language manuscript from which the German translation was made, except that I have somewhat expanded Chapters 5 and 7. I want to thank Deutsche Verlags-Anstalt for their generosity with respect to surrender of certain publishers' rights, and also for their kindness in making available to Doubleday & Company illustrative material originally produced for the German book.

I found the opportunity to write the book during the 1968–69 academic year, while at Cambridge, England, on sabbatical leave from Michigan State University. My warm thanks are due to Professor Sir Nevill Mott and Dr. R. J. Eden for their hospitality at the Cavendish Laboratory, Cambridge, during this period. I am indebted to Professor J. H. McKee, of Purdue University, for his helpful comments on a first manuscript, and I thank Miss Carol McCall, then of the Cavendish staff, for her expert typing of the final manuscript. I am grateful to my wife, Sally McKee Schlegel, for her cheerful assistance with much of the routine work associated with production of the book.

Over a period of more than three decades I have had the benefits of instruction and friendship from my teacher in the philosophy of science, Professor Herbert Feigl. I wish, as an expression of appreciation, to dedicate this work to him.

East Lansing, Michigan, 1971.   R.S.

INQUIRY INTO SCIENCE

1

THEME OF THE BOOK

Activity in science is the primary distinguishing characteristic of our era. We should not think that it is only in the
past few hundred years that men have been advancing our
knowledge of the natural world through science; for, in
fact, the science of the modern period is built on notable
scientific achievements of medieval, Greek, and even ancient Babylonian and Egyptian civilizations. But nonetheless, science and the application of science are the activities
in which we of today clearly excel all previous cultures.
Greek sculpture, medieval architecture, and eighteenth-
century music, as examples, are hardly surpassed by current efforts in the arts. But our twentieth-century science
is completely without parallel, both in what it has achieved
and in its organization for further extension of knowledge.

The ascertaining of the structure of the atom, the
elucidation of the complexities of molecules of both living and non-living materials, the exploration of the stellar
universe, with hopes even of comprehending its entirety,
the development and use of abstract logico-mathematical
systems: these are a few of the broad ways in which science has met the challenge of understanding nature. Further, it is apparent to all that the applications which have
been made of the new knowledge have enormously
changed ways of living in the industrialized nations.

Science itself, instead of being an esoteric vocation of
a select few, is coming to be an everyday concern of a
substantial fraction of the people of the world. Science

education is being introduced as part of the elementary education of children everywhere. And in the United States, for example, the number of people who are involved in scientific research and development, at all levels, is approaching 5 per cent of the working population, whereas the number who are primarily engaged in farming is in a decline that is approaching that same fraction. This fact is a particularly impressive illustration of the importance of science, since even with so relatively small a farming population the United States is able to produce more food than is needed by its own people. Such a high productivity is largely a result of the application of science to agriculture.

Great as have been the changes effected by science in our external ways of living, these changes are perhaps less than those in our way of looking at the world. Most educated people now have an essentially naturalistic view of themselves and the universe. Even though tradition and experience may give people a religious conviction, they now rarely seek immediate explanation of natural phenomena in terms of supernatural powers; instead, appeal is made to the structure and regularity in nature that have been discovered by the scientist. Certainly in the control of nature we rely—and with impressive justification—on science. Here success has come not only with respect to inanimate nature but also, in medical science for example, for the biological realm. And to a considerable degree we even look to science for the guidance that was once the prerogative of the priest and the ethical philosopher; thus, the psychologist gives counsel about the maintenance of a marriage or the rehabilitation of criminals.

The unquestioned usefulness of science seems itself to give a warrant for its validity as knowledge of nature. Considering how great our increase in that knowledge has been, and how firm the prospects are for a continuing growth, we may well ask the question, "Will science go on until it has described and explained the entire universe?" Or, an alternative way of putting the question is, "Can we expect that science will eventually be *com-*

plete, such that we can gain from it the answer to any question we ask about the natural world?"

Many varied opinions have been given with respect to these questions. Some physicists have suggested that certain fields of physics—for example, the electronic structure of atoms—are even now essentially complete. But others have emphasized the highly partial and selective nature of the physical knowledge that we obtain. There are those who see science as the only road to knowledge and as the necessary base for the progress of mankind; others today speak of science as having shown itself to be of no value in leading human culture to a better estate. The variety of points of view that have been expressed by thoughtful people is an indication of the complexity of the question that we ask. And indeed, we cannot hope to come to any simple "yes" or "no" answer about the completeness of science.

But in this book we shall systematically consider various aspects of science and of the philosophy of science which bear on the questions of limits and completeness of science. By doing this we will learn some definite things about necessary limitations on science. In certain other respects we will find that we must leave questions open. We should, though, be able in the end to reach a fairly clear understanding of how science does have definite limitations and yet also unending possibilities that are related to the nature of the universe itself.

My first step will be to discuss the structure of science. For, if we are going to examine how far science can go, we must first have in mind some idea about what science is. We shall then go on to the possibilities and limitations of science as description of the natural world. There are certain limits, we shall see, that arise from the nature of description, but others come from what we have in fact found the natural world to be. The discoveries on the level of the very small, in what we call quantum physics, will be important to us here; and, at the other extreme, we must also give some attention to the physical studies of the cosmos, in the science that has come to be known as cosmology.

Besides discussing descriptive, factual aspects of science, we shall want to consider how the nature of scientific explanation affects the limitations of science. We will therefore have to discuss the logical, deductive aspect of science; this is the property of a well-developed science whereby statements about nature may be deduced by methods of logic or mathematics from general theoretical assertions. Scientific explanation, we shall see, can be successfully given for wide domains of nature because of the deductive properties of scientific systems. But also these same properties contain certain inherent factors limiting the completeness of science.

Generally in my treatment I shall be using both an approach based on what we know the structure of science to be and one based on the established content of science. The completeness-of-science problem obviously involves what kind of knowledge science gets and how it organizes that knowledge. But the nature of the world, as discovered by science, must also be relevant. If, for example, the universe were found to be a relatively simple, finite entity (which it has not been), the outlook for completeness would be different than for the immensely complex, possibly infinite universe that has so far actually been disclosed by science. So we cannot talk about limits of science only in terms of the nature of science, but we must involve the findings of science.

In addition to the logic of science and the content of science there is a third element which we must not neglect. I will call this the pragmatic factor in the limits of science. It arises not so much from what science is or discovers as from what people in practice actually want from science. We shall see, in a word, that a limit arises in a field of science simply from the particular interest or need of those who are creating the science.

There is, however, one practical aspect of science which is of the highest importance but which I shall not regard as within the scope of this book. It is all too clear that applications of science have today brought not only great benefits but also many serious problems. The pollution of air, earth, and water that come with industrialization, the threat of catastrophic nuclear war, the ill as well as the good that can come with effective medicines are some obvious examples. It might quite properly be taken that in discussing the place and limits of science one would emphasize such problems, for reason of their importance in the continuing life and happiness of mankind. But there is a limit, too, on the number of topics that can be discussed in a book, and we shall not try to go on, beyond the problems of limits in science itself, to questions of what might be the completeness of applied science.

Armed with the conclusions that we shall have come to about science, we will finally consider what the relations are between natural science and man's activities in the arts, literature, philosophy, and theology. Occasionally men have been so blind as to regard the significance of these humanistic pursuits as trivial; and those sympathetic to the arts have sometimes falsely dismissed all of science as being only of relevance to the material aspects of living and not to problems of mind and spirit. What we have discerned in this book about the nature of science will give us a basis for making a statement of the relative roles of the scientist and the humanist. I hope that because what we say does rest on an analysis of the domain and limits of science it will have more conviction for the reader than would a simple assertion of opinion.

2

THE STRUCTURE OF SCIENCE

Science is altogether a human activity. It may seem unnecessary to say this, but it is a point that I want to emphasize because people sometimes believe that science is objective and independent of persons in the same way as is nature itself for the most part. In fact, although science describes nature, it is obvious that an essential component of science is contributed by the scientists who develop it. The changes which occur in our scientific outlook, as new facts are uncovered and more adequate theories are developed, give abundant evidence of the human origins of science.

The human activity that is basic to science is observation; and a respectful regard for the results of observation, beyond any interest that might come from philosophical speculation or emotional bias, is fundamental in the work of a good scientist. But we cannot say that observation alone will make science; for the senses can bring us a myriad of impressions, and we must select certain ones for attention. We order the potential chaos of sense impressions through the use of concepts which—if well chosen—should correspond with structures and regularities of nature.

The role of concepts in ordering our observations is important at what we call the concrete levels of experience, as well as in more abstract thinking. Consider, for example, so simple an object as a stone lying on the ground. In order to discern it as a separate object, distinct from the earth on which it lies, we must have in mind an idea that identifies the stone as an object with certain properties (as hard, crystalline, non-metallic) and with a certain name ("stone"). Nature has formed the stone with these properties, and as an object which may readily be separated from its surroundings as an individual object, but it is man who has chosen to identify and name it as such an object.

The word "construct"—introduced into the philosophy of science by Professor Henry Margenau—is useful for describing the relation between physical object and idea. Thus, we can think of a stone as being a construct, in that we have in our minds an idea (properties and name) which enables us to identify a stone. But also we will say that the construct has the same existence as does naturally existing stone. The denotation or meaning of the construct, then, is *both* the stone which we observe in nature and the idea or concept which we have of it. It may well be that our construct is not as complete or adequate as we like; new observations might, for example, tell us that the property "always sinks in a liquid" is not true for a stone if the liquid is mercury. Hence, the natural stone is much, much richer in properties than is the construct which we have set up. But nonetheless the construct serves very well for enabling us to pick out and discuss certain features of nature.

Science is a construction of language; that is, it is presented in terms of ordinary language (English, German, etc.) and mathematical symbols, graphs, photographs, etc. It is by means of constructs that we are able in science to describe the natural world. When we say "stone," we refer to the object in nature but we discuss it not by passing around a literal stone but by using the construct, stone, which is also a verbal symbol that has significance and connections with other symbols in our minds. So, it is because the construct is both in nature and in our language that we can use it in science (or in ordinary everyday description). An analogy is helpful here. The soap molecule is roughly rod-shaped; one end is a fatty acid that is soluble in oils and the other end is salt-like and

Elements of the Natural World

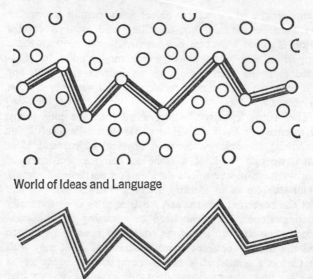

World of Ideas and Language

FIGURE 1 The construct is formed from selected aspects of experience and often with additional postulated or inferred elements. It is in the natural world, but also, it is *in accord* with an idea or concept; hence, it is both in nature and in man's linguistic-mental realm.

soluble in water. Because of these properties the soap molecule can dissolve both in water and in oil and hence is useful in dissolving or "cutting" greases and oils with water. Similarly we can see the construct, with its being both part of nature and part of man's linguistic-mental equipment, as the medium for joining the natural world and the linguistic realm of scientific description. It allows the miracle that man is not bound to his own physical being, but can in speech and thought freely roam over the entire natural world.

The formation of constructs for clearly demarcated objects, as a stone or a flower or an animal, is so obvious that we directly think of the object as a separate entity. In science, however, many of the constructs are by no means so obvious. We can, indeed, think of the genius of science as being, to a large extent, the discerning (we could even say the invention) of constructs which contribute to description and understanding. For example, the electron is never directly seen, but there are various natural and experimental phenomena which are consistently explained by the assumption that there are entities with the properties that we postulate for the electron. For indirectly inferred objects such as electrons we sometimes use the term "concept," and thus refer to the concept of the electron. But nonetheless we do believe in the existence of the electron, and it is therefore a construct in the sense that we have defined that term; i.e., the electron is both a concept implying certain definite properties and an element of the natural world. (See Photos 2 and 3.)

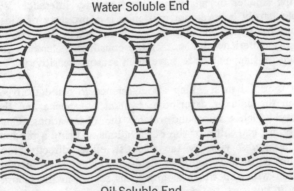

Water Soluble End

Oil Soluble End

FIGURE 2 Soap mixes oil and water because one end of the soap molecule associates with water whereas the other end associates with oil. Analogically, the construct, which is both in nature and in the mind, brings together the natural world and the realm of thought and language.

For the scientist the question of the existence of anything that he has postulated reduces to a question of learning whether or not experience (usually indirect) shows that thing to have the properties postulated as being associated with it. Thus, the electron is required to have mass and charge. We find in any experiment involving the electron that it does have these properties; and, in fact, observation has taught us that it also has two other properties, spin (angular momentum) and magnetic moment, which were not initially given to it as a construct. When the properties which the scientist requires for existence of an entity are found by observation, no matter how indirectly, he generally believes that entity to exist quite as much as do the constructs of daily experience. Thus, we believe atoms, electrons, protons, mesons, and electromagnetic waves to be altogether a part of the natural world, even though we do not see them directly. It would be difficult to justify a belief to the contrary; for we have abundant evidence that the everyday objects of direct experience are made up of the smaller objects which we know by inference. We could hardly believe that existence is a property of those things for which we human beings happen to have direct sensory experience but not of the constituent elements for which we happen not to have such sensory sensitivity.

It is useful in speaking about science to distinguish between the data or descriptive content of science and the theory which unifies and relates the observations. Generally, we can think of the observations as being a product of literal observing by the scientist, either directly from nature, as in astronomy or field-work botany, or in connection with experimental apparatus set up in the laboratory. In contrast, the construction and utilization of theory is an activity of the scientist in which he makes use of accounts of observations but is working only with pencil and paper, and commonly with the assistance of formal mathematical reasoning. But, useful as it is, the observation-theory distinction is by no means an absolute one. We in fact do not have "pure" empirical data in science, with no reference to theory, and also we can hardly have theory without some content from observation. This latter point will probably be readily granted, since a scientific theory is concerned with observed elements of the natural world. But the assertion that we never have a purely empirical statement in science is not so obvious.

Scientists sometimes talk about "hard fact" as opposed to mere theory, as if nature gave us immutable, unquestioned factual data. In a sense this is so, in that an immediate observational result if carefully made should be the same for all people, anywhere or any time. But we must remember that what we observe is very much determined by what theory suggests should be observed; and we must remember also that the way in which an observation will be reported and interpreted is a function of the theory that is in the observer's mind.

Observations of the planet Jupiter from Earth, for example, have been interpreted in many different ways. For an astronomer who accepted the Ptolemaic theory of planetary motions, the apparent changes in position of Jupiter were clear evidence of its cyclic movement about the earth. For us today, the same observations tell us that the planet is in orbit about the Sun. For men of non-scientific cultures, various mythological ascriptions were probably given to Jupiter. It is to be granted that our contemporary theory almost certainly gives a better account of the motion of Jupiter than did any previous theory; still, what we have today is a theory, not immediate fact. Even the interpretation of a given sighting of Jupiter as indicating a certain position for it in space does involve the assumption of the theory of the straight-line propagation of light in a uniform three-dimensional space (an assumption that is in fact not rigorously correct in the terms of Einstein's theory of gravitation). And so it is with any other bit of observational evidence in science: a close examination will show that a theoretical point of view is presumed in the statement of the evidence. We have seen that even in the everyday observation of a stone there is a theoretical content; for, the discerning of the stone as such involves the construct, which can be regarded as a kind of theory, that there are small, hard, non-metallic objects which are separate from the body of the earth.

We must see science, then, as being a complex, interwoven structure of theory and observation. A scientist is emphasizing the latter when he is carrying out observations and experiments, but he virtually is never working without the guidance and understanding that come with theory. When a science is in an early stage of its development we usually find that its theoretical part is rudimentary, or perhaps is not much different from the commonly accepted everyday theory for the phenomena that form the field of study of the science. It is in this period that a science is referred to as being highly empirical, or perhaps even as being a "set of unco-ordinated facts." Thus sociologists have learned many facts about the social behavior of people and about social institutions. But, without at all wishing to deny the worth of efforts that have been made toward developing a social theory, we can say that there is today no developed theory by which we can firmly understand and predict social phenomena. In contrast, in a highly developed science, theory formed in the science has come to be established as valid in its own right; and this theory both describes natural phenomena that have been observed and allows predictions to be made for the future course of natural events. Some of the central parts of physics (excluding certain newly developing branches which might well be in a "fact-gathering" stage with respect to the domain under study) are prime examples of a highly developed science. The science of mechanics, for example, involves a small number of basic laws, and from these the behavior of mechanical systems of all kinds can be deduced, given the physical forces which are involved.

A science which has a close logical structure approaches the form of what is known as a deductive system, although generally it is only in mathematics and logic that we have explicitly formulated systems of this kind. The elements of a deductive system are: i) a set of primitive terms or

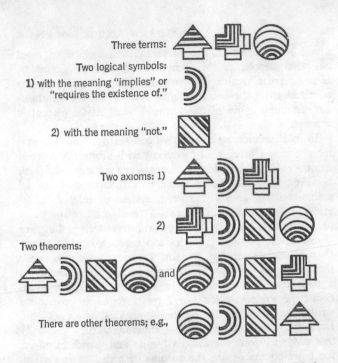

FIGURE 3 A simple deductive system is illustrated. Mathematics is a highly complex and powerful deductive system. In natural science basic principles have the role of axioms from which special cases may be deduced (generally with the assistance of the deductive methods of mathematics).

symbols with which *all* the terms and symbols that make up the system can be defined; ii) a set of postulates or axioms; iii) rules of inference in accordance with which we can make deductions from the axioms. A simple syllogism is an elementary deductive system. Thus, if I state as postulates "all men are mortal" and "Socrates is a man," I can deduce, using the ordinary rules of logic as rules of inference, that "Socrates is mortal." Here the words that I use are the primitive symbols, and the one deduction or theorem of the system is "Socrates is mortal." A much more complex deductive system, known to most educated people, is the system of Euclidean geometry. Here a great wealth of theorems (deductions) may be obtained from the basic axioms: indeed, an infinite number, although many of them would be of trivial geometric interest.

In mathematics, and logic, we can set up deductive systems among a given set of symbols with arbitrarily formed axiom-sets, and see what deductions are consequent. Even, however, in as formal a science as mathematics not all axiom-sets will give a deductive system of interest. Generally, the axioms must express a tenable model or point of view with respect to the primitive terms that are involved; or, perhaps it is not too much to say that they should embody a new insight. In natural science, even though we do not usually formulate a science explicitly as a deductive system, we might say that we have quasi-deductive systems. For we have systems of equations written as relations among basic physical concepts, and from the equations we derive statements (or "results") that give us information about the natural world. In effect, the basic equations are the axioms of a deductive system. And in science they, of course, must faithfully state an actual structure or relationship in nature if they are to form a correct scientific theory. The testing of consequences of the equations through experiment and observation constitutes a major way in which the validity of the equations is established. Other requirements include internal consistency of the equations, consistency with other already established parts of science, and tenability or adequacy of the basic concepts involved.

The laws of mechanics, as already indicated, are a good example of a deductive system in science. Given Newton's three laws relating mass, velocity, acceleration, and applied force—with the laws put into a suitable mathematical form—we can describe and predict an enormous number of different physical phenomena. The motions of the various bodies of the solar system, the precise behavior of earth satellites, the trajectories of projectiles, the oscillations of pendulums and of vibrating springs and rods, the effects of frictional forces, the behavior of flowing liquids in various situations: these are a few, and many more could be named. It is true, however, that the "axiom-set" of Newton's laws does not suffice to describe relations between motion and force throughout nature; when speeds close to that of light are involved the modifications of the theory of relativity must be introduced, and for small masses, on the level of the atomic world, the extensive changes introduced by the quantum theory must be considered.

Maxwell's equations for electrical and magnetic fields are another example in physics of a deductive system, even though they are not put explicitly in that form. As far as we know the equations describe and predict all electrical and magnetic phenomena that are on a macroscopic (large-scale) level. (Here, too, on the atomic level where we consider individual electric charges the equations alone are not adequate.) The quantum theory of atomic structure may itself be considered to be a quasi-deductive system. Other branches of physics are sufficiently organized mathematically that the physicist operates with them essentially as deductive systems in which he finds physical consequences from postulated equations. In biology the theory of evolution does function in a qualitative way as a basic postulate which is used in the description of natural processes. Thus a set of closely related but different fossils is organized into evidence of a time-evolving living species, on the basis of the theory. More generally, the great array of different living organisms is understood in the light of the theory of evolution, and to a slight extent even prediction of future biological change is made on the basis of the theory.

We can see science, then, as having two major modes of procedure. One is the exploration and discovery of the natural world: the extension of our descriptive knowledge of nature, we might say. The other is the establishing of general laws or equations which will bring the descriptive knowledge into a coherent, deductive theory. But we stress again that the two procedures are not independent of each other. We must have empirical data about the world in order to form a theory, but also we need to have the generalizations of a theory to guide and interpret our accumulation of data. The ideal result of the two procedures would be a completely deductive system in which every natural event that comes within the domain of a science could be seen as a consequence of its general laws or equations. These would themselves give us general knowledge about the domain, and an understanding of them would give a sense of understanding for that part of nature. Thus, knowing Newton's law of gravitation gives us in a single generalization an immense advance in understanding the natural behavior of macroscopic material bodies. We have pointed out that it is only for a few domains of nature that we have achieved such completeness, notably in certain fields of physics. But we shall consider in Chapter 6 what limitations remain on science even if we should have an ideal completeness for all of science.

Finally, I want to return to the opening theme of this chapter: that science is a human activity. The role of constructs in science shows us how much man does contribute to the formulation of scientific knowledge, particularly as it becomes more abstract. What nature is, does of course put constraints on what scientific theory is. But we are not justified in thinking that a given theory gives us the only way of talking about the aspect of nature to which it is relevant. There almost certainly could always be alternative theories, based on a different set of concepts (constructs) and employing different formal relationships. Once a theory becomes well established, we tend to think that its primitive constructs are "as given in nature," but such a belief is illusory. The ideas of mass, force, and acceleration that are used in modern mechanics seem, for example, to be "natural" and obvious. And yet it took the genius of Isaac Newton to define them and demonstrate their utility as foundations for a science of mechanics. Thus Aristotle, even with all his intellectual in-

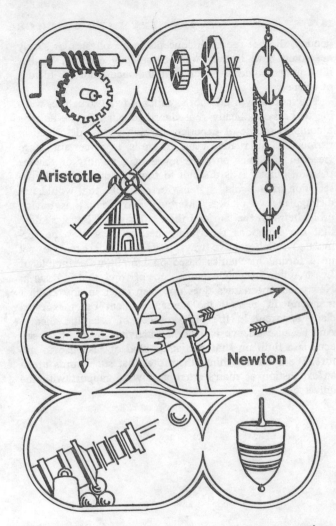

FIGURE 4 Aristotle thought that a force had to be continuously applied to a body to keep it in motion; his conclusion was a natural consequence of observations of bodies that were moving against frictional retarding forces. Newton's concept, that a body naturally continues its state of motion or rest as long as no force is applied, came with a discerning understanding of inertia and empty space.

genuity, did not use such concepts in his physics, as surely he would have if they were completely obvious. Similar illustrations could be given in abundance from the history of science.

The natural world is not so much a fixed structure, waiting to be symbolically reproduced in our science, as it is a complex source of experience which can be described in various and alternative ways. There is, to be certain, more freedom of choice on some levels of generality of science than on others. It is difficult to think of any scientific description of the solar system, for example, that would not distinguish two planets (Mercury and Venus) as having orbits between the sun and the earth's orbit. But we know that the equations describing these planets may be formulated in alternative ways. (We can, for example, set up a formal mechanics based on Hamilton's Principle of Least Action in which the concept of force that is basic in Newtonian mechanics does not even enter in any explicit manner.) In general the human element becomes especially apparent in the high reaches of scientific theory. And because science is a human activity any limit on science is a limit on that particular kind of response to nature. We need not think, therefore, that such limits mean an exhaustion of man's attempts toward rapport with the universe.

3

LIMITS ON SCIENTIFIC DESCRIPTION

Since the first task of science is to give us information about nature, we might reasonably think that the ultimate goal for a particular science is for it to contain a statement of every fact that concerns its domain of nature. Even aside, however, from the problems of knowing what "every fact" might be, we can readily conclude that such a goal is an impossible one. Suppose, for example, that we set out to develop the complete science of the chemical element sodium. We would want to know the appearance of sodium, its chemical properties, the many chemical reactions into which it enters, the manufacture and use of it. And its various physical properties such as density, thermal and electrical conductivity, thermal expansion, optical reflectivity, bulk modulus, as well as others, should be measured with as high a precision as is possible. Also, we would want a statement of the atomic structure of sodium, and of its behavior in interactions with electromagnetic waves (atomic and nuclear spectra). But all of this general information would be but a beginning, for it would have been of sodium as a general entity. For a complete scientific description, as specified, we would also want to know the location of every piece of sodium. Indeed, if we accept literally the goal of "every fact," we would want to specify the location of each atom of sodium in the universe and, in addition, the relationship of that atom to other kinds of atoms (position in molecules, etc.).

We readily see what a virtually hopeless task it would be to complete a science for just one constituent of nature. But in a complete science, as defined, not only sodium but every other component must also be described. Further, organized collections have properties that are not present in the individual components; thus, to take an obvious example, a biological organism has properties that belong to the entire organism and not to each entity constituting it. So each such organism, as well as inanimate object such as a telephone, or the earth, or the sun, must also be described.

It is clear that we cannot expect in science to state every possible fact; nor does it even appear necessarily desirable that we be able to do so. It is of interest to note that in addition to the obvious practical difficulties of attaining complete scientific description there is a logical block. Because of this barrier we are able to assert without reservation that it is impossible to make such a description. The logical difficulty comes with the fact that every time we write a piece of scientific description, it itself—in a rigorously complete description—would become part of the world that should be in the complete scientific description. Suppose, for example, that sentence 3, paragraph 258, volume 124 of the sodium series in our science should describe the sodium in one of the rocks of Stonehenge. That sentence is now part of the world and should therefore itself be described in a complete description. But then this new describing sentence would again require description, and so on. We see that we come to an infinite regress which prohibits our ever being able to include a description of the last describing sentence.

The limitation that comes with the impossibility of describing every description may seem to be a trivial one, but we shall see in the next chapter that a somewhat analogous situation exists as an aspect of limits on physical description in quantum physics. Also, we do today see how the descriptions of science require descriptions of themselves, in that library material (much of which is descriptive science) must be properly catalogued. And even "bibliographies of bibliographies" are not unknown. As descriptive knowledge grows, the problem of managing accumulations of material becomes increasingly difficult, as librarians well know.

The impossibility of complete description also suggests the interesting philosophical conclusion that the world cannot be completely aware of itself; that is, there is no possibility of an awareness or recording of every detail of the universe. If consciousness were an inherent property of every bit of matter in the universe we could not argue against a thorough self-awareness. But in fact consciousness appears to be a property of an organized group of atoms that form an organism with purpose, response, and memory. Specifically, the mechanism of a nervous system seems to be required for consciousness. Likewise, any machine that describes, or that stores information, requires a complex mechanism. Hence, awareness or description requires elaborated mechanisms which are themselves subjects for further description. Complete awareness of the universe would require, then, that an organism or mechanism be able to direct its attention to the external world and also to its own self while taking that cognizance of something other. But such a dual awareness seems contradictory; one again comes to the infinite regress of "awareness of one's self taking cognizance of one's self being aware of . . .", etc. We arrive, therefore, at a naturalistic argument against a complete self-awareness of the universe.

Even though we cannot expect science to be complete in a description of some universal aspect of nature, we can set up a limited domain in which description may approach completeness. For example, we might have an interest in a single particular crystal. Its physical properties could be measured with great care, and, by methods of electron and neutron diffraction and use of electrostatic-field photography, the detailed arrangements of atoms in the crystal could be studied.

There are, it is true, certain inherent physical limitations on the fineness of physical measurement, which we will be discussing in the next chapter. But excepting for those limits, which appear only with magnitudes of atomic dimensions, we can usually find a way to increase the accuracy of a physical measurement. What is involved, generally, is a question of how much further effort we are willing to give. Thus we may have found for our crystal, to an accuracy of one part in a hundred, the constant which expresses how rapidly the crystal will conduct heat. We could almost certainly gain a measurement accurate to one part in a thousand, and then perhaps go on to the still greater accuracy of one part in ten thousand, and so on. The determination of thermal conductivity coefficients, as these constants are called, is however a notoriously difficult matter experimentally because of the problems in preventing unwanted heat losses and gains. More elaborate apparatus can bring closer measurements, but the rapid rise in amount of work and ingenuity required will generally discourage the effort to go beyond a certain degree of accuracy. If, however, we did for some special reason want still greater accuracy we probably could find a way to obtain it.

The completeness of description that we find in science results, then, from limiting that which is to be described to a selected domain of nature. And we obtain completeness not in any absolute sense of having described every possible detail, but only in the sense of having described as much as we find worth while within the necessities of our science at a given time. We see here the importance of what I call pragmatism in our conception of a complete description; the purpose for which we want a description will to a large extent determine at what point we consider it to be complete.

The selection of domains for description may be made for one of many different reasons. Even with the traditional goal of increasing our knowledge of nature, the scientist's choice will be strongly affected by his particular competence and interest. Thus a zoologist interested in animal morphology, a physiologist concerned with reproduction processes, a biochemist studying carbohydrate metabolism, and an ecologist studying dependence of biological species on environmental changes will all study a given animal species with different resulting descriptions. (See Photo 4.) Also, some parts of nature may recommend themselves for investigation simply because of their striking aspects: thus, lightning, volcanoes, the aurora borealis, the rainbow, a symptom of disease. In these instances a selection for description may be guided by little more than an inherent interest in the phenomenon. Frequently a natural entity or process may be exhaustively studied for the sake of the role it plays in a theory, as a critical confirmation or exemplification. The close study that has been given by physicists to the speed of light is an example, as is, also, the elaborate investigations by geneticists of inheritance and chromosome structure in the fruit fly, *Drosophila*. Some research may be for the purpose of a suitably defined kind of completeness and for no other apparent reason: a botanist may wish to catalogue all the kinds of native plants in his county; a chemist may wish to prepare and study every known compound of a given element; a classical scholar might devote his life to writing an exegesis on every extant work of a chosen Greek author.

It is just because nature is so varied and complex that limitation is necessary if progress is to be made in a given field of science. Otherwise, the scientist would have a confusing jumble of facts. If the physicist, for example, considered not only the masses of bodies in a mechanical investigation but also their geological origins he would clearly be encumbered rather than assisted. Or, likewise, the human physiologist who recorded data on the political beliefs, as well as on the chemical composition of the blood, of subjects under study would probably be adding unnecessary confusion into his data (although we must recognize that scientific discovery does often consist of the discerning of surprising relationships). It seems clearly to be the case that we make progress in science not by initially investigating the entire cosmos but rather by selecting aspects of nature for which there is some common, limited structure or process. The physicist attends to those

abstract physical properties which are part of matter
and radiation everywhere in the universe; the physiologist
limits himself to a particular aspect (natural biological
processes) of a certain set of natural objects (living organisms).

But the choice of a domain for scientific description may
also be made for purposes that are other than an interest in
obtaining knowledge as such. These purposes are as varied
as those which operate in life generally. Food production,
military strength, medical therapy, better transportation,
faster communication, social improvements, personal or
institutional prestige—these are some of the motives that
may give rise to a search for scientific description. And
here again, the scientific activity that is carried on for each
of these activities is, of course, directed to a limited aspect or domain of nature. The agriculturist interested in
food production possibilities of a new land and the cartog-
rapher interested in preparing a detailed survey map are
each going to "see" and describe different aspects of the
land in the light of the goals they have in mind for the
particular scientific work they are doing.

Several centuries ago the term "natural philosopher"
was used for the scientist who at that time could take all
parts of nature as appropriate for his investigations. Today we have a division of science into hundreds of different
fields, each concerned with a limited domain. The number of specializations increases continually as new aspects
of nature are studied and as the growth of knowledge
brings further subdivisions in already established fields.
The success of science in answering to man's intellectual
and practical needs brings about this proliferation of new
specialties; and, indeed, science concomitantly has become
for many not so much the philosophical search for truth
about the universe as the practice of a challenging and
rewarding profession.

Keeping in mind that in practice we generally do not
have "science," but have a "science of" some limited aspect of nature, we can propose a definition of completeness in science that avoids the impossible "describing every

fact" goal. We will say that *a science is descriptively complete when as much descriptive detail as is desired has been achieved for the domain that is defined for the science.* We now ask the question, Can a science reach the limit of having given a complete description of its domain of nature? With the new definition of completeness we can in a meaningful way look to the actual state of science for answers.

Some sciences do in fact seem to be reasonably complete. The physical geography of England, for example, has a clearly defined but limited purpose: the setting out of the topography of England with detail that is sufficient for those who are living in or studying that country. When we have considered the maps that are available, it seems correct to say that in terms of our definition this is a complete science. For Earth generally, physical geography is not yet a completed science, although air surveys appear rapidly to be closing the gap. For the moon, particularly the far side, a physical "geography" is, obviously, only in its beginnings.

As an example of a not so highly empirical science we can consider inorganic chemistry. The domain of this science is constituted by the chemical properties of the elements and their compounds, with the exclusion however of the hydrogen-containing compounds of carbon (which form the domain of organic chemistry). In its techniques and fundamental concepts the science merges with physical chemistry and physics at many points, but in chemical practice and literature there is clearly a distinct separation of the explicit study of the elements and their inorganic compounds. With the establishment of the periodic table as a valid classificatory scheme, and the description of the readily obtainable compounds, the science achieved a fair degree of completeness. I do not wish to imply that the completeness is absolute even with our definition. New and interesting aspects of inorganic chemistry have appeared in recent years: thus, transuranium compounds, complex stereochemical molecules, noble-gas compounds, and new insights into chemical bonding. Inorganic chemistry is clearly alive as a research field, and practical uses for various types of new compounds assure continued practical as well as scientific interest. Yet, if one's interest is dominantly that of understanding the salient features of our natural world, I believe one can say that the science has achieved its major goals, and we therefore could speak of its relatively high degree of completeness. But we readily see how much completeness in a science is related to what is desired. For an inorganic chemist whose primary interest is the synthesizing of a ceramic with novel properties of strength and heat resistance the science might not seem at all to be complete.

The mathematical science of plane trigonometry provides a somewhat different example. Here the domain is a limited one of the relations between magnitudes of sides and angles in triangles. The relations that one might expect to obtain have been found, and a great deal of specific information about these relations has been calculated and tabulated in tables of trigonometric functions. The science is not complete in the sense of containing a recording of every last possible detail; this could not be achieved in a finite world, since the values of each trigonometric function could be calculated to an indefinitely large number of decimal places and for an indefinitely large number of specific angles. However, in terms of the definition that I have introduced, completeness has been achieved. Trigonometric functions are usually known with as much accuracy as is desired for purposes of calculation, and, further, methods are available for finding them to greater accuracy if that should be desired.

Sometimes there may be a strong desire to advance knowledge in a science, but work may virtually cease in it because there seem to be no feasible ways of gaining further information. In such a case one would not properly say that the lack of activity in the science implied that it was complete, excepting perhaps if there were virtually no prospect, even at any future time, for definite advance in the science. For example, during the first half of the twentieth century astronomers in general (with, to be sure, some notable exceptions) gave little attention to the physical characteristics of the planets of the solar system. All persons interested in science would probably have liked to know much more than was available about the planets, but astronomy seemed to have gone about as far as it could in gaining information about planetary surfaces and atmospheres. Still, no one would have been likely to say that our knowledge of the planets was complete. Then, in the mid-twentieth century the development of space-exploring rockets, as well as of new techniques in spectroscopy and radio astronomy, gave us new knowledge of the planets, and the prospect that with sufficient effort further desired knowledge could be obtained. As a result there was a great heightening of interest in the planets throughout astronomy. We would today describe planetary astronomy as a very active but highly incomplete science; fifty years ago it could perhaps have been characterized as both incomplete and inactive.

One should be cautious in offering an example of a science which might be called complete because there are no prospects for further knowledge. The future course of science is so unpredictable, and there are so many instances in the past of unexpected break-throughs to new domains of natural knowledge, that one hesitates to suggest that no more can be gained in any one field of knowledge. We shall see, later, that science itself demonstrates certain fundamental limitations that prohibit certain kinds of further knowledge. But perhaps the safest example can be taken from studies that are of specific human beings and their activities rather than of the broader natural world directly. Thus we would like to know more than we do about the life of Plato. The possibility of important new material coming to light cannot be ruled out, but it seems fairly likely that the field of Platonic scholarship is complete in the sense that we shall not gain further significant information. Another example might be provided by an ancient city whose ruins have been thoroughly studied by archaeologists, with no remaining prospect for further information.

The responsiveness of science at any given time to factors of feasibility, current trends of interest, and social demands emphasizes again the human origin of science; it is a structure of knowledge that grows in those places to which scientists have directed their labor rather than in accordance with some objective plan of nature. We can say this without overlooking either the circumstances that some aspects of nature more obviously call to man for scientific investigation than do others, or the prime fact that the specific content of the structure of science is not arbitrary but should be in accord with properties of nature.

Since science is made up of particular fields, each limited both in its domain of study and in its desired descriptive detail, we can see science generally as having a limit built into its very organization. But the limit is peculiarly two-sided: it can be seen either as a falling away from an ideal completeness or as a constraint that may give the potentiality for complete fulfillment. If we have in mind as a goal of science the laying out of a complete description of every last detail of the natural world, then, as we have seen, science is indeed disappointing, for its limitations clearly prevent it from ever reaching that goal. On the other hand, the limited expectations of science, as it is actually practiced, do allow the attainment of a completed science within those expectations. The completeness is not likely to be more than approximate, and certainly provisional, for new discoveries or new interests can quickly change what was a tolerable completeness in a science into a glaring insufficiency. (Thus, scientists were reasonably content with regarding atoms as indivisible ultimate units of matter until Becquerel's discovery of radioactivity in 1895 opened up the problem of the structure of the atom itself.) But still, we can have satisfaction in the possibility that a given part or aspect of our world can be scientifically studied and a desired amount of information may be obtained about it: an amount which may be reasonably sufficient both for satisfaction of curiosity and for purposes of control.

However, we have by no means completed our story. Even with the limited descriptive goal which I suggest obtains for a science, it does not follow that scientists necessarily will be successful in *every* aspect or domain of the universe which is set up as a field of science. Specifically, there are two obvious fields where we might expect a barrier to even limited description; these are in the realm of the very small, as we go to the level of the atom and below, and in the domain of the very large, where we try to consider the entire astronomical universe. We shall now, in the next two chapters, treat of what we have learned in science about the possibilities for descriptive completeness in these domains.

But before going on, I should also say a word about what is another lack in our discussion so far. For the sake of simplification I have talked about the gathering of information into descriptive science without discussing the concomitant theory-construction aspect of science. But we saw in the previous chapter that descriptive fact does not stand by itself; that it only gains its meaning in a context of theory. We may emphasize description in science, as we have been doing, but likewise we may emphasize scientific theory. Hence, we must talk about limits of science in terms of the theories that scientists develop as well as in terms of descriptive fact. Theories are especially relevant for explanation, generalization, and understanding in a science, and we shall also find that for these features of science there are limits. However, first we must explore yet further the limitations that we find on descriptive scientific knowledge.

4

LIMITS ON ATOMIC DESCRIPTION

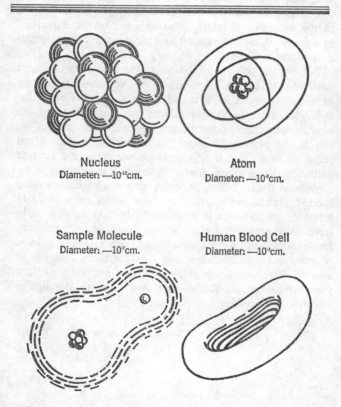

Nucleus
Diameter: —10⁻¹²cm.

Atom
Diameter: —10⁻⁸cm.

Sample Molecule
Diameter: —10⁻⁷cm.

Human Blood Cell
Diameter: —10⁻³cm.

One of the most notable achievements of science in this century has been the disclosing of the small-scale structure of matter. Physicists, chemists, and, in recent years, to some extent biologists have shown us the complexity and order among atoms formed into molecules, and then on a smaller scale for the electrons and nucleus in the atom, and on still finer scale among the protons and neutrons in the nucleus itself. A molecule may consist of anywhere from two to millions of atoms, with each atom having a diameter of about 10^{-8} cm. The particles which make up the atom have, in turn, dimensions of about 10^{-12} cm. Should we expect that we can continue downward to yet smaller particles of definite size and location? One of the surprising results of modern physics is that there is a definite "no" in answer to this question. Knowledge of matter on a smaller scale is not beyond question—and in fact in some ways has already been obtained—but it is not knowledge of structure, with fixed space-time position, of the kind that we have in our world of everyday dimensions.

The basis for the study of the small-scale aspect of nature is contained in what we call quantum physics, which has its conceptual framework in the quantum theory. This latter is one of the two great theoretical developments in twentieth-century physical science, the other being the theory of relativity. In quantum physics—and this means in our study of the fine-structure of nature—there is an all-important role for the quantum of energy. It has been found that in any interaction between physical particles or between particles and radiation (e.g., light) there is a necessary transfer of a minimum amount of energy. This minimum will in general not be so small a value physically as is possible mathematically; that is, we do not have a

FIGURE 5 Some sizes on the microscopic level and below. Quantum physics has told us that we come to *necessary* limits in the detail of space-time description as we go into the realm of the very small.

continuum of possible energy transfer values, as had been assumed in the pre-quantum theory days. The minimal energies involved are called *quanta,* and the singular *quantum* for an individual interaction gives the quantum theory its name.

The consequences of the constraint on interaction energies are remarkably far-reaching. Energetically excited atoms, for example, cannot give up radiation of *any* wavelength (the emission of radiation is itself a kind of interaction), but only in *certain* wavelengths that correspond to physically prescribed quanta of energy. Hence we find a sharp-line spectrum of emitted radiation from the atoms in a gas, and, also, the electrons in an excited atom can only be in those energy levels (or "orbits") which correspond to the allowed quantum differences in energy levels. Another notable effect of the quantum rather than continuous nature of energy changes arises with the fact that observation is always an interaction and hence involves an inevitable energy transfer and disturbance.

A quantity known as Planck's constant, usually symbolized as h, determines the magnitude scale of the quanta in physical energy exchanges. Thus the energy of a photon of light, the irreducible unit of light energy, is hf, where f is the frequency of the light. The value of h is 6.6×10^{-27} erg-seconds (an erg is a unit of energy equal approximately to the work in lifting a mosquito through one centimeter!). Clearly, remembering how small is the fraction 10^{-27}, we see that quanta are trivial indeed on the level of interactions between human-size things. It is for this reason that only with a fairly sophisticated science did physicists come to the subtleties of quantum physics.

The consequences of quantum theory for the description of nature may be summed up in one of the basic concepts of the theory—the Uncertainty Principle. The principle was enunciated in 1926 by Werner Heisenberg, and shown by him to follow from other parts of the theory. For our purposes we may write it in the following two equations:

$$\Delta x \cdot \Delta p_x \geqq h, \qquad (1)$$
$$\Delta E \cdot \Delta t \geqq h. \qquad (2)$$

Suppose a particle is to be located along a spatial dimension, taken as the x-axis. Any uncertainty in the localization is indicated in Equation (1) as Δx. Suppose we wish to measure not only the position x of the particle but also at the same time its momentum p_x in the x direction. (Momentum is the mass m of the particle multiplied by its velocity v; thus, $p_x = mv_x$, where the subscript x is used simply to indicate "in the x direction.") We write any uncertainty in determining the momentum as Δp_x. Now Equation (1) tells us that there are necessary uncertainties in the position and momentum of the particle, such that their product is at least Planck's constant h. That is, we can never *exactly* know both the position and momentum of a particle, in a given direction. In the ideal limiting case of, for example, $\Delta x = 0$, we would then pay for our exact knowledge of position x by having no information at all for p_x, since Δp_x would have to become infinitely large in order to satisfy the equation (infinite momentum-uncertainty would mean that the particle might have any velocity from zero to the speed-of-light limit, c).

Equation (2) expresses a similar limitation on information, but now for the energy E and time t of an event. Suppose that we wish to observe the time at which a radioactive atom emits an electron, and also to learn what is the energy of motion of the emitted electron. Now Δt is the uncertainty in the observed time and ΔE is the uncertainty in the measured energy. The Heisenberg equation asserts that we cannot know both t and E as accurately as we wish. There will be a necessary uncertainty in both the time and the energy of the emission-of-the-electron event. Again, achievement of zero uncertainty for one of the quantities, time or energy, would be at the price of loss of all information about the other. (Photo 5)

Before discussing the limitations in the gaining of information which the Uncertainty Principle introduces on the level of atoms and sub-atomic particles, we should try to gain some understanding of what properties of nature require the principle. The way that I have worded this proposal does itself make a first point: the Uncertainty Principle follows from the nature of the physical world. Although in practice there are limits to the accuracy of any measurement, we have earlier emphasized that greater refinement in the measurement is generally obtainable. The Uncertainty Principle, however, tells us of an inherent limit which cannot be overcome by any elaboration of measurement apparatus. Since the principle is basic in the structure of quantum theory, if measurements were made that did better as regards accuracy than is allowed by the uncertainty equations, we would have to conclude that quantum theory is fundamentally in error. The quantum theory is, however, strongly established, both in factual basis and through confirmation of predictions.

It is a basic tenet of the theory that generally the various possible physical states (e.g., of position and velocity) in which a particle may exist determine the behavior of the particle, except when the particle as a result of an inter-action-observation goes into some one single state. This property of being distributed among various possible states is not one that we find for the behavior of a particle in non-quantum physics. But further, if the behavior of the particle with respect to some one property, e.g., spatial position, is determined as a result of its going into a single state (location), there is another property, momentum, for which the particle must remain in all the various possible (momentum) states. That is, the particle cannot simultaneously make the change from the behavior that goes with a composite of many states to the behavior of being in a single state, for both the property of location and the property of momentum. The influence on behavior from the various possible states in respect to a given property, when the particle is not in a single state, is the Superposition Principle of quantum theory.

In the theory we can see the incompatibility between single-state behavior for specific pairs of properties (in effect, the Uncertainty Principle) as coming from basic physical incompatibility. Light, for example, impinging on a shield with two slits (FIGURE 6) may pass through either slit "a" or slit "b." The light must then, by the Superposition Principle, be regarded as coming to the screen with the properties of having come both from a and from b (i.e., of being in both the states "originated in a" and "originated in b"). As a result, the interference pattern of light and dark bands which is actually observed is predicted by theory. But we also know from experiment that if we "localize" the light, by having it strike a photographic plate

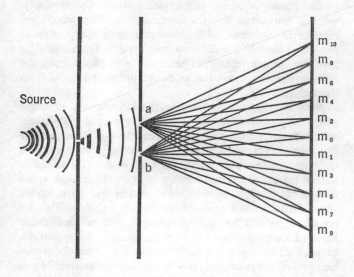

FIGURE 6 Double-slit interference. Light coming from the slits "a" and "b" forms a series of light bands at m_0, m_1, m_2, etc., with bands of darkness (absence of light) in between. Light bands result from constructive interference (crest on crest) between two sets of light waves, one from each slit, whereas the dark bands arise from destructive interference (crest on trough) between waves from one slit superimposed on those from the other.

placed in the "a" or "b" position, we would find the light to be photons which pass through either one or the other slit but not both. The very act of such a localization would destroy the superposition of the two states that gives rise to interference. Conversely, the possibility of passage through both slits gives the interference but does not allow the localization of light in the form of a photon that passes through one slit only.

We have in the experiment just described an illustration of the celebrated wave-particle dualism. We have the same effects with matter: with, for example, a beam of electrons passing through different possible slits (as may be formed by the planes of atoms in a crystal lattice). Or, similarly, we find variations in light intensity, or, alternatively, in number of electrons, at a shadowing by a sharp edge of opaque material; the different path-lengths from the edge give rise to interference (Photos 6A and 6B) among the light or electron waves just as do the different lengths from the different slits.

Now to make the passage to the Uncertainty Principle —in a very qualitative way—we can say that if the photon, or electron, is localized in a given slit we have lost the specification of momentum which gives the particle a definite wave property that will lead to interference. For nature does seem to tell us that in moving through space a material particle as well as a photon has an extended wave form, with a momentum that is equal to Planck's constant divided by the wavelength. But a localization means a concentration of the mass energy of the particle, or photon, at a point, with loss of information about momentum. On the other hand, if the particle is traveling as a spreading wave of a certain wavelength and momentum, spatial localization, as to a given slit, is lost.

We can appreciate intuitively that an entity cannot simultaneously be an extended wave and also a mass point; hence there is a necessary restriction on the possible simultaneous determination of both spatial position and the property that is associated with wavelength and motion, that is, momentum. Niels Bohr enunciated the Principle of Complementarity as a statement of the impossibility of observing, in a given physical context, two variables which are mutually exclusive in an Uncertainty Principle relation. Thus, in the illustration that we have been using, one might have one experimental arrangement for determination of light interference properties, but this would exclude an arrangement in which one determined the photon localization by interrupting the passage of light at one of the slits with photographic film. The two arrangements would be complementary; although it is impossible to observe both the wave and corpuscular (point-like) behavior in one apparatus, each aspect gives information that adds to, or complements, the information given in the other.

We might want to ask, "But cannot we do experiments that tell us what are the fundamental properties which cause a particle to have the curious behavior of seeming to move as a wave and yet acting as a corpuscle when it is in an interaction?" For such an elucidation, however, we should have to have sources of information about the microscopic particles of nature other than the particles themselves, and this we do not have. On the levels of magnitude that are above the quantum dimension, we can learn of nature through the medium of microscopic particles. Thus, light rays are reflected from a tree and tell us of its shape and color without in any way changing the tree; or, a cell in an electron microscope interrupts the beam of electrons with a resulting production of a density pattern that is an image of the cell. However, when we wish to learn about an electron itself, an electron or an entity of comparable magnitude, such as a photon, must bring the information to us. But an electron that is being studied as a wave, say, cannot tell us anything about itself as a particle, or vice versa. The same barrier applies to the properties of a photon, from which we might hope to get information about an electron through the photon's having interacted with it: the photon, as a wave or as a particle, can bring information about the effect of an interaction with the electron, but only for the electron as one or the other. Further, we cannot get information about an electron as it "truly" is without the effect of an observation-interaction. This effect can never be nil because of the non-vanishing value of the quantum of energy transferred in an interaction. That is, it must be the electron acting both as object O and as medium I that brings us information; or alternatively, if some other entity, such as a photon, is the medium I, it so changes object O in its interaction with it that it brings a message OI rather than simply O.

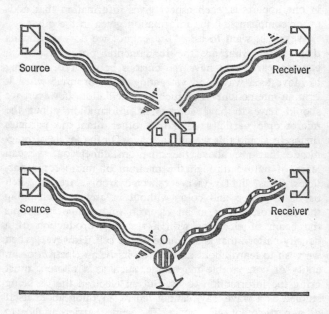

FIGURE 7 On the macroscopic level of everyday things we can observe an object without significantly affecting it. Thus, photons (light) reflected from a house bring us information about its shape without disturbing it. But a photon which brings us information about the location of an elementary particle, on the quantum-physics level, also imparts motion to the particle.

Logically, there is no reason why very small entities that can delineate the details of electron behavior should not exist. Physically, our experience has told us that nature does not allow anything with such a function. Even if sub-electronic particles should be discovered, their constitution and behavior would be such, we believe, that the basic uncertainty relations would apply to them also and they could not give measurements that would overcome the Uncertainty Principle limitations on our knowledge of the electron. The uncertainty in description of atomic particles does not arise *only* because of the effects of interaction in any observation of the particles, but also, because the quantum properties of particles are such that the description of their behavior requires the utilization of various physical states, of which one state is taken up by the particle when it is observed. The wave-particle dualism is a particular manifestation of this indefiniteness of state, described by the Superposition Principle. It is this principle which prevents a formulation of a theory that would make possible exact description through calculated allowance of the effects that occur with interaction-observation. In general, there is no predicting, except in terms of a statistical probability, into which of the superimposed states the particle will go at the instant of the observation event.

Quantum physics has uncovered a limit to the descriptive range of natural science. We are accustomed, in everyday life, to giving a specification of the position and time of objects, and until about forty years ago it was a presumption in science that this kind of space-time description could be carried on indefinitely into the realm of the very small. The Uncertainty Principle equations show us that it cannot be; that when we come to dimensions and energies such that Planck's constant h is not a comparatively trivial quantity, we cannot expect to achieve precise description in terms of space and time variables. The uncertainty equation that relates position and momentum shows us explicitly that we cannot simultaneously describe location and velocity. We find from the energy-time equation that an increase in time accuracy is at the expense of increased indefiniteness in energy. Calculation with the equations leads, further, to the result that specification of position alone also requires energy uncertainty (a not un-expected relation, since momentum is related to energy). Hence, the simple spatial (i.e., location) description of a particle cannot be made arbitrarily precise, unless an infi-nite amount of energy is available. For example, the un-certainty equations show that an electron, even if its "self-energy" mc^2 be considered to be available, cannot be de-scribed within spatial dimensions as small as those of an atomic nucleus; for this reason we never expect an electron to "fall" from the family of outer orbiting electrons in an atom into the nucleus itself.

An ancient philosophical inquiry asks whether matter can be sub-divided indefinitely, into smaller and smaller pieces, or whether the process must somewhere stop with bits of indivisible matter. Immanuel Kant regarded the question as one of the antinomies of reason, since he could give what appeared to be conclusive arguments either way. However, the limits that nature itself puts on space-time description now show us the resolution of the prob-lem; as we come to sufficiently small dimensions, we find that the concepts of space and time with which we asked about divisibility and indivisibility are no longer applica-ble. We can justifiably say that, in the terms in which scientific knowledge had been sought for many hundreds of years past, we have come to an end of the search. The limits reached are both an indication of possible complete-ness with respect to space-time knowledge, on the micro-scale, and a caution that such knowledge can go only so far.

I do not want to say that we should now expect that physicists can learn nothing more about the smallest par-ticles of nature. But we can conclude that beyond a cer-tain point further knowledge will not be of traditional space-time structure and process. We cannot expect that the electron, say, will be analyzed in a manner similar to that in which physicists and chemists have discerned the positions and relations of various atoms in complex molecules. Currently, work is being done on the *internal* structure of protons and neutrons; but the pattern that is inferred from the observations is a rapidly fluctuating one, with only a probability assessment for a given structure (in accordance with the Uncertainty Principle).

Within the limits of quantum physics, there can still be a seeking for knowledge of the properties of particles, the nature of their interactions, and the kinds of forces that operate. But different goals have largely replaced the older aim of space-time description: the physicist has new interests in principles of invariance (of what is unchanging in structure and form in nature's elementary processes) and in principles of symmetry (of what is independent and what is dependent with respect to direction in space, in time, or alteration in electrical charge or in energy). We must find understanding of the basic physical entities in terms of concepts such as these, because it would be hopeless to expect to gain the kind of knowledge that we have in non-quantum physics for the macroscopic world.

It was widely accepted among scientists in the nineteenth century—and the roots of this idea go back to the Greek natural philosophers—that nature in all respects changes in a deterministic way. Every state of a chosen system, or equally the entire universe, was assumed to be required to be precisely as it is by the preceding states. The solar system, for example, given the present positions and velocities of the planets and of every other particle in it, could one hundred years from now have but one state, definitely determined, for every object in the system (assuming no external disturbances). The laws of pre-quantum physics, expressed as they were in space and time variables which presumably were unlimited in their exactitude, gave support to an acceptance of complete determinism in nature. But with the changed expectations for knowledge that come with quantum physics we have reason to change our attitude. Suppose a system, isolated from outside influences, to consist of a small number of interacting elementary particles, with the laws that govern the interactions between the particles known to us. We wish to predict the state of the system at time t from knowledge that we have of it at t = 0. But because of the Uncertainty Principle limitations we cannot exactly know the state of the system even at t = 0, in the old sense of knowing both position and velocity of each particle. At best we can have only knowledge of probabilities for values of these variables. Clearly, then, we cannot make predictions for a later time t, except, again, in terms of probabilities.

We can see the breakdown of determinism in quantum physics in a yet more fundamental way. The equations of quantum theory describe the behavior of a system, e.g., a

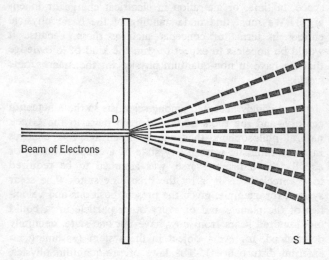

D

Beam of Electrons

S

FIGURE 8   Because of their wave property, electrons in passing through a very narrow opening (D) are spread out just as is a light wave (see also FIGURE 6). There is nothing in quantum theory that allows us to calculate more than a probability for an electron's striking the screen S at a given point; that is, we can make no exact calculation, and, we believe that the exact behavior of an electron in nature is not determined.

particle, with a recognition in the calculations of the presence of all the various possible states of the system. (This is the Superposition Principle, already discussed.) But which *particular* state the system will be in as a result of an observation being made of it is never predicted by the theory (unless only one state should be known to be relevant). Thus, in the two-slit experiment we could never expect to learn from the *theory* whether a given particle, or a photon, can be interrupted by a measurement made at slit "a" or at slit "b." All we learn from quantum theory is the probability of finding the system in a given state, when we make a measurement: e.g., the probability of observing the particle at "a" or at "b." It is, therefore, a general characteristic of quantum physics that knowledge of individual events can be ascertained only through observation. This property is in strong contrast to non-quantum physics, in which we do predict individual events with certainty, and feel justified in asserting their occurrence even if there has been no observation: e.g., the passing of a moon of Jupiter through a given point in its orbit, hidden from our view. Since in quantum physics we have no predictive theory with respect to individual events, but have knowledge of such events only through the immediate act of observation, we clearly do not have any warrant for asserting a relation of determinism among events.

Of course, the changes from a deterministic view that are required by quantum physics are, at least in the first instance, only on a level of the very small. We find that for an ensemble of many atomic particles, the equations describing its behavior approach the same form as in non-quantum physics; that is, for macroscopic bodies the probabilities tend toward certainties for those events which would be predicted in non-quantum physics. The prediction of a given eclipse of the sun, for example, is not in the slightest degree impugned by the considerations of quantum theory. Nonetheless, physical processes on the microscopic level can have consequences on a much larger scale. We could arrange that if a photon activates a de-

tector at slit "a," for example, a machine which opens
one door is set into motion, whereas the photon at slit
"b" causes a different door to open. In the biological realm
it may well be that chance events on the micro-level give
rise to gene mutations which in turn cause major devia-
tions from the normal in the mature organism.

The evidence that we now have against strict determinism suggests a striking change in our philosophical
outlook with respect to past and future. With a belief in
determinism, one had to see the universe as set for all time;
nothing that now happens could in any way change what is
to happen, since each state of the universe must inexorably
follow in every detail from preceding ones. The deterministic universe might be likened to a long row of completely
finished but darkened stage settings. The play of a search-
light, passing from one setting to the next, gives each a
moment of being the present state of the universe. Con-
ceivably, one could know what all the settings are, and in
effect have predicted and retrodicted all future and past
states. In contrast, with a measure of indeterminism on
the quantum level, we can expect that large-scale features
of sets that are not too far removed in time will be related
to whatever is the present setting, through necessary and
calculable relations. But small differences, not subject to
rational inquiry, can occur even between immediately
neighboring sets, and such differences may give rise to
long-run changes of major magnitude. We cannot expect,
then, that a precise development of, say, a given animal
species is pre-determined (even though the properties of
nature would put on certain general constraints).

The relaxation of determinism that comes with quantum
theory seems to bring physics into an agreement with our
intuition that was lacking with a completely deterministic
science. For certainly we do feel that within our own small
spheres of influence we can change the future by what
we do in the present. The apparent existence of quantum
indeterminism has, in fact, been advanced as a physical
basis for free will in human activity. I think we should be
cautious in such an assertion; our knowledge of the mecha-

nism of conscious determination of behavior is not great enough to allow us to see in any detail what is the relevance of the physical indeterminism that has been established. But it does indeed seem valid to say that this indeterminism on the micro-level severely weakens the case of those who assert that there can be no freedom of the will.

Finally, I want to show how the quantum limits on description have brought us reason to accept a kind of atomic finitude in nature. Until a few hundred years ago men had virtually no knowledge of objects smaller than those that can be directly discerned with the human senses. The microscope opened up an entire new realm: a complex, populous world of tiny living cells and organisms. Today our knowledge of the molecular-atomic structure of matter brings us to yet another level of being; the decrease in magnitude is about ten times more than the decrease in going from man to the dimension of the one-celled organism. There is still another drop in size, by about the same factor as from the single cell to the atom, as we consider the elementary particles that make up the nucleus. It has seemed to many people that this successive series of smaller structures might go on forever, with always a new and smaller domain of structure to be found (somewhat like an unending series of Chinese blocks, each fitting inside another). The recurrence of certain patterns in nature gives credibility to this idea. Thus, the atomic nucleus surrounded by orbiting electrons has a similarity in structure to the sun and planets of the solar system; or vast galactic "dust" clouds sometimes seem to be similar in form to clouds formed in our own terrestrial atmosphere. The speculation has been advanced by, for one, the philosopher-mathematician A. N. Whitehead that there may exist sub-atomic worlds with sentient beings and whole civilizations as complex as our own.

But as we go to smaller dimensions we do in fact find a barrier against the stable existence of structured entities. This comes from the Uncertainty Principle: as we have seen, decrease of the spatial extent in which a particle is localized requires an increase in the range of momentum available to the particle. Energy and momentum are closely related, so that in effect any sharpening of localization requires higher energy. If, for example, we were to postulate a complex structure within a proton, which has a diameter of about 2.4×10^{-13} cm, we would be considering entities which can be localized within distances of, say, 10^{-15} cm. But generally we simply do not find energy in nature sufficient to provide that degree of localization. It is true that the energy-time uncertainty equation would allow high energies for very brief times, and one might plausibly argue that what is a short time to us is long on a much smaller scale of being. But these brief flashes of localization would not be coherent for an ordered structure of entities; if they were we would expect to detect the coherent ensemble of all the energies that were required. Our conclusion from quantum physics must be that as we go to smaller dimensions the world that we know of ordered structures in space-time must give way to sub-nuclear entities that rapidly fluctuate in and out of existence, without ever having precisely defined space-time boundaries such as we find for a man, a crystalline solid, or even for a molecule.

One might wish to argue that the sub-realm consisted not of localized particles but of extended entities, of low energy and hence within the bounds of what is physically plausible. That is, the requirement of a sharply defined structure for the hypothetical entities might be dropped. Here, however, we would have two alternatives. The new entities could be regarded as so completely different from the physical particles and fields which we know that they would be unresponsive to any of our detecting instruments. But we would then be postulating entities which are in a world unknowable to us, and therefore not within the manifold of natural science. We may imaginatively construct any realm of being that we like, but unless there are relationships between that realm and our world of experience the construction is not one that is of relevance to the natural world. The second alternative is that the

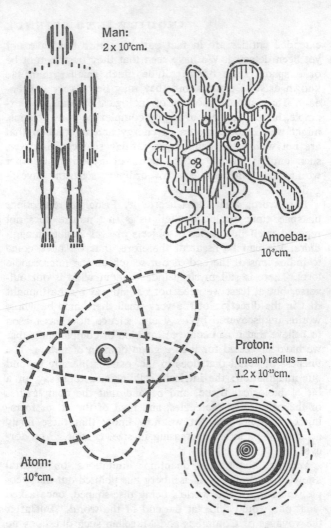

Man:
2 x 10²cm.

Amoeba:
10⁻²cm.

Proton:
(mean) radius =
1.2 x 10⁻¹³cm.

Atom:
10⁻⁸cm.

FIGURE 9 We descend by factors of about 10^{-5} as we go from the linear dimensions of man through single cell, atom, and proton. There is an upward jump, by a factor of about 10^7, from man to the diameter of the earth, and then a huge upward increase, by a factor of about 10^{14}, from the earth to the diameter of our Milky Way galaxy (10^{23} cm.).

extended entities are in fact part of nature but have not yet been detected. We have seen that they then cannot be of a spatial scale of magnitude much smaller than the known existent entities, but they may be of very low energy. The natural processes of biological systems, for example, including those of highly complex nervous systems, might well involve modes of energy and interaction that are not within the ken of present-day science. However, such entities would not be parts of hypothetical other worlds but rather subjects for ordinary scientific investigation.

In a word, what the Uncertainty Principle restrictions on space-time localization tell us is that nature does not repeat herself in a series of objects of ever smaller magnitudes. We can be assured, therefore, that we have come to indications of the end of our search on the microscopic level. There is still mystery indeed about what is our universe, but at least we need not be haunted by the thought that in the direction of the very small there may be whole worlds undiscovered by us. Here, science now has reason to believe that it can come to the kind of completeness that we have suggested for it in a given domain of nature. The fineness of detail that does in fact exist is literally beyond our imagination: the intricate cellular structure, say, of a bit of biological tissue, and beyond that the complexities of the constituent molecules, and then of the atoms forming each molecule. But we now know that these finely articulated patterns, decreasing in size, cannot go on forever.

Writing about the quantum limitations on natural knowledge, Professor Heisenberg has pointed out that people, thinking of the world's being disc-shaped, once asked what one would find "at the end of the world." But after the voyages of Columbus and Magellan such questions no longer made sense, even though much of the earth was still unexplored. So it is for us today on the quantum level of nature. There are myriad detailed questions of nuclear, atomic, and molecular structure yet to be answered, including important problems of molecular-biological organization. And the quantum physics has itself raised fresh problems which physicists are hoping to answer by going into the novel realms of elementary particles at very high energies. But certain questions, we have learned from quantum theory, need no longer be asked.

The problem of "how can a flat earth end" was solved by our learning that there is no such problem, because a spherical earth has no "ends." Similarly, the problem of the infinite divisibility of matter has been solved as we have learned that at certain points we must change our basic physical ideas: that nature does not allow us to project the properties of macroscopic bodies to indefinitely small magnitudes. The solution to the problem came, we see, not in the terms in which we had been asking it, but after we discerned the new constructs which are required by nature for adequate discussion of the problem. We may appreciate the understanding that we now have of the limits on the very small, both for its own intrinsic value and as illustrating that even the most difficult questions may not be hopeless if cast in terms that are valid constructs of nature.

5

COSMOLOGICAL LIMITATIONS

I want now to make an about-face and turn from the world of the small to the domain of the very large. We have seen that on the microscopic level science has come to a natural limit. Should we expect to find a similar result in the other direction: that there is a finite end to the universe of galaxies and radiation, such that we can regard our science as able to comprehend the total universe? The branch of science which attempts to study the over-all properties of the astronomical universe is known as *cosmology*. This word is also commonly used to describe an outlook or set of beliefs with respect to the whole range of basic questions about what is man and his universe, and, as such, cosmology is generally a mixture of science, myth, and religious doctrine. Every culture, it is often said, has some sort of cosmology of this broad kind. In current science cosmology has come, however, to have a relatively more restricted meaning; it refers to the efforts of physical scientists to discover what is the total extent and spatial structure of our astronomical universe in its large-scale aspects, and also, if possible, what has been its past history. So—and this is perhaps what is appropriate in our Western culture—by cosmology we shall mean a scientific enterprise carried on chiefly by interested astronomers, astrophysicists, and mathematicians. It is in their work that we can hope to see to what extent science might be successful in discerning the structure of the total universe.

Modern knowledge of the astronomical cosmos may be

taken as beginning with Copernicus' arguments in the six-teenth century for the existence of a sun-centered system of planets. Once his conception had been established, Earth had to be regarded as being but part of a much larger uni-verse and not the central cosmic body. The physically in-significant dimension of Earth on an astronomical scale became increasingly apparent as astronomers established more details about our stellar universe. Today we know that our solar system of the sun and nine planets is itself part of an immense galaxy of about a hundred thousand million (10^{11}) stars. We call this great structure the Milky Way galaxy; it is roughly disc-shaped, of about 100,000 light-years in diameter, and we are looking sidewise through the disc when we observe the dense band of stars in the heavens that we call the Milky Way. The solar sys-tem is situated about three fifths of the way out from the center of the disc.

Vast as is our Milky Way galaxy, it is but one of many galaxies that we can observe in any direction in which we look out into space. Only the nearer ones are visible to the naked eye, and they only faintly; for, even though a galaxy is large enough to contain billions of stars, there is generally a separation of several million light-years be-tween neighboring galaxies. Telescopes, however, reveal an indefinite number, and one of the prime problems of cosmology is to determine whether or not the universe of galaxies goes on forever.

Until about fifty years ago, there was very little observa-tional or theoretical content with which to make up a scientific cosmology that encompasses—or seeks to encom-pass—the entire astronomical universe. But discoveries of the past few decades, reaching far beyond our own Milky Way galaxy, have given some astronomical evidence that can be brought to bear on various cosmological models that have been devised. The theoretical construction of such models in cosmology has proceeded chiefly on the basis of the pioneer work of Albert Einstein. In his general theory of relativity he showed that the gravitational force which exists between any two bodies in space is associated

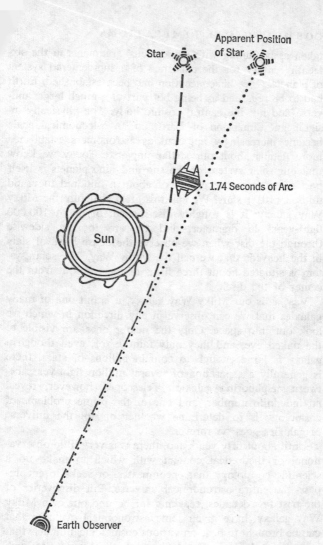

Star

Apparent Position of Star

1.74 Seconds of Arc

Sun

Earth Observer

FIGURE 10 The bending of starlight caused by the sun's gravitational force (curvature of space). The light rays pass close to the sun, and are regarded by the earth observer as coming in a straight line; hence the star image is displaced from its true position.

with a slight curvature or deformation in space-time. The curvature goes intrinsically with any element of matter, and decreases with distance from a mass in very nearly the same way that gravitational force decreases with distance. There is, for example, a slight curvature of space associated with the sun: a curvature which is great enough, close to the sun's surface, to cause a passing light ray (as from a star) to be very slightly bent out of its usual straight-line path. This effect has been observed and is one of the empirical confirmations of the relativity theory.

The first observations of the light-bending were made on May 29, 1919, at Sobral, in Brazil, and on the island of Principe, off the west coast of Africa, by English astronomical groups sponsored jointly by the Royal Observatory and the Royal Society. On that date, and at those places, there was to be a total solar eclipse, and it was hoped that the effect, if genuine, could then be detected. The space curvature is very slight, and an observation of it could only be expected for starlight which passes close to the sun and therefore experiences an extremely strong gravitational field (with associated spatial curvature). And stars can be observed close to the sun only at the time of total eclipse. Even for such observations the predicted deviation by the light from a straight-line path is only 1.74 seconds of arc.

A photograph taken of the star field with the eclipsed sun in it may be compared with a photograph of the *same* star field, taken at another time when the sun is elsewhere in the heavens. The two photographs may be put into congruence, using star points that are far from the sun on the photographs (and hence undeviated); the stars that are very close to the sun in the eclipse photograph should then be deviated by the predicted amount, if the theory of relativity is correct. The measurements—even with high precision mechanical aids—are close to the limits of observation, but the 1919 results did emphatically support Einstein's prediction! This confirming observation, incidentally, seems to have initiated the intense world-wide interest in the relativity theory, and in Albert Einstein, which has been so prominent a feature of twentieth-century intellectual life. There have been other observations of the bending of light, and recently (1970), measurements of radio waves passing close to the sun, from a quasar source, have beautifully confirmed the 1.74″ prediction. There is, with radio waves, the great advantage that they can be observed in close proximity to the sun's position at any time (rather than only during a total eclipse).

Einstein also found that in addition to the "local" curvature associated with material mass, the equations of the theory require a slight "global" or over-all space curvature. The degree of this curvature is determined by the magnitude of the average density of matter in space, and Einstein found that he could relate the over-all geometric character of the universe to the matter and energy that are in it. With this relationship one can hope to infer from observations (if sufficiently extended) what is the structure of the universe. The viewpoint that is adopted in these cosmological considerations is one which overlooks all but the very large aspects of our observable universe; commonly, the elementary unit of matter is actually taken to be a grouping as enormous as a galaxy, somewhat as a molecule is the unit of matter in the theory of properties of a gas.

I shall not attempt to survey all of current cosmology, but I will present a few salient features that will help us in estimating the possibilities for completeness in the science. One clear and indisputable fact about our world is that the night sky presents a dark background, against which we see the moon and stars. This darkness of the night sky has the important implication that there is a significant element of finitude about our universe, as is shown by an argument known as Olbers' paradox, after the German astronomer Heinrich Olbers, who presented it in 1823. Suppose that our universe did extend infinitely in space, with everywhere approximately the same concentration of stellar matter that we observe in our sample of the universe; also suppose that the universe has existed forever with about this density of matter and radiation. Olbers' calculation shows that then the night sky would not be dark but would be blazing with light. The reason is that although light decreases in intensity with the inverse square of its distance from a source, the number of sources goes as the third power (the cube) of the radius in a sphere of approximately constant density of sources (stars or galaxies).

To express the situation in a rather crude way mathematically, we can say that the number of light sources is proportional to R^3, where R is the distance from an observer, since the volume of a sphere is $\frac{4}{3}\pi R^3$; and the intensity of light from any one source is proportional to $\frac{1}{R^2}$. In a sphere of radius R, no source is farther than R from the observer. The product of number of sources and light intensity determines amount of light received, and this product, we see, is roughly proportional to R. So, as the radius R of the volume containing light sources becomes indefinitely large, the light coming to an observer increases indefinitely.

Hence, if space, with light sources in it, extends on forever from an observer, light intensity will build up without limit at his point of observation. In actuality, we would expect an equilibrium to be reached between the light and surfaces of the stars, so that the light intensity in the sky would be about the same as the mean intensity at the surface of stars. The presence of absorbing matter in space in the form, for example, of dust particles would not alter the situation, since with the high radiation intensity these particles would be expected to come to the same glowing temperature as the mean stellar surface temperature.

But since we do have a dark night sky, we can say with confidence that the universe is in some sense restricted in its infinity. Two obvious alternatives are that: i) the universe is infinite spatially but was created a finite time ago, so that light from very distant galaxies has not yet reached us and brightened our sky; ii) there is in some way a spatial finitude about the universe. Generally, cosmologists

have been loath to accept the first alternative. Creation of
an infinite universe, a finite time ago, seems to be an event
which is counter to the evidence that we have for natural
change and development. We have found in nature that
the state of any domain, at a given time, seems to have
arisen through a continuous process from states at preceding times. Hence, creation of the whole universe as a
single event appears to require a discontinuity that would
be out of accord with the way of nature. So, unless compelling evidence to the contrary should become manifest,
cosmologists will undoubtedly keep their study of the history of the universe within the confines of established natural processes. (Of course, if evidence for a creation event
were found, there would surely be an attempt to bring the
creation process itself within the scope of natural law.)

The second alternative—that there is an element of spatial finitude for the universe—has been supported by observation. But, as we might expect, the character of this
finitude is not simple, and not even its prime characteristics
are definitely known and understood today. We have not
found that we can, in a direct way, say, "Yes, the universe
is finite, with such and such an extent"; or, alternatively,
"The universe is infinite, and extends without end." But
we should not be surprised at complexity; it is hardly to be
thought that an inquiry into spatial finitude for the entire
universe will have the same kind of simple answer that we
can give when asked, say, the dimensions of a box, or
even of a galaxy.

The major observation relevant to spatial finitude is the
celebrated "red shift" of distant galaxies. Light is emitted
from atoms that are part of a hot gas (as in a star) at
definite wavelengths, corresponding to different colors if
the radiation is in the visible range of the electromagnetic
spectrum. It has been observed that the radiation of all
but nearby galaxies, as seen from Earth, is shifted toward
the red end of the visible spectrum (i.e., toward longer
wavelengths). Our established physical principles tell us
that this shift means a recessional motion—that the galaxies
are moving away from us. Further, the observations show

that the more distant the galaxy the faster is the rate at which it is speeding away from our galaxy. This fact may be expressed in terms of an equation,

$$V = HD,$$

where D is the distance of a galaxy, V is its observed recessional velocity, and H is a constant, known as Hubble's constant, after Edwin Hubble, the American astronomer who established the velocity-distance relationship. There are astronomical methods for estimating distances D, and the value of H has been found to be such that for each million light-years of distance from us a galaxy has a recessional speed of about 25 km/sec. Observations have been extended to very distant galaxies, with recessional motions that are about two thirds of the speed of light.

The galactic motions provide a necessary element of finitude, as required by Olbers' argument. Even if the universe is infinite, the light from faraway galaxies will carry little energy because their recessional motion causes a decrease in the radiant energy of each photon received from them; and from those at the speed-of-light limit, the light coming to us would carry no energy at all. Hence, we find the night sky to be dark: the universe that we can observe is essentially a finite one, even though conceptually it could be part of an infinite extension.

Theory and observation have not stopped, however, at a simple notion of a manifold of galaxies receding from our point of observation. We should, in fact, not think of our galaxy as being at the center of the expansion. Mathematical analysis shows that if the galaxies are everywhere receding from their neighbors at some given rate, it will appear from each galaxy that all the others are receding at a rate proportional to distance. We can easily see the required motion in one dimension by considering points laid out along a line of indefinite extent. Suppose that every point is moving away from its nearest neighbor at the same rate. Then, for example, say that at t = 0 adjacent points are everywhere 1 cm apart, that at t = 1 sec they are 2 cm apart, at t = 2 sec they are 3 cm apart, and so on. For

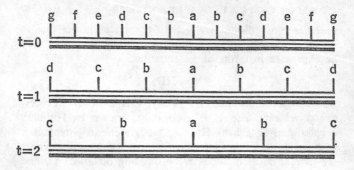

FIGURE 11 A one-dimensional illustration of how Hubble expansion appears to occur in relation to any chosen point. The points on a line move so as to be separated by an additional centimeter from their two nearest neighbors in each second; from any arbitrarily chosen point the recessional velocity of any other point will then be proportional to its distance.

any point a that we choose on the line the neighboring two points b will have a recessional speed of 1 cm/sec, since they must move a distance of 1 cm in 1 sec. The points c (FIGURE 11), originally twice as far away, must move away with a speed of 2 cm/sec. For points d the speed with respect to a will be 3 cm/sec. We see that the simple Hubble relationship, $V = HD$, between distance and speed holds for the recessional motion of all points from any one point, and yet no one point is preferred as a "center of motion" over any other point. In this one-dimensional model we assume either an infinitely long line or a position sufficiently far from the end of a finite line that the "observer" does not see the end.

One wonders, is the expansion which we actually observe in the galactic universe occurring at a rate that is constant in time? In principle we can answer this question from observation, because when we see distant galaxies we are seeing them at an earlier time. There is some evidence—but it is not conclusive—that there has been a decrease in the rate of expansion over the past several billion years.

As I have already noted, the Einstein theory of relativity gives a relation between space and matter in space. Since this theory has been confirmed for relatively nearby astronomical phenomena there is no reason to doubt its applicability on a cosmological scale; it is taken therefore as the basic theoretical tool in cosmology. The theory ascribes to space a scale-factor which can change with time. Thus, consider two galaxies which are separated by so great a distance that "local" motions which each galaxy may have can be neglected; that is, from a consideration of motion in their own neighborhoods the two are approximately at rest with respect to each other. In an expanding universe, however, the cosmic scale-factor prescribes that the distance between the galaxies is increasing. (If the universe were static, or contracting, the scale-factor could likewise be stationary or decreasing.) In considering the mutual recessional motions of the galaxies, then, we do not think of them as moving apart in an unchanging space, but, rather, as being carried apart in consequence of the expansion of space. An analogy with the surface of a balloon is helpful. If there are painted dots on the balloon, they will move away from each other as the balloon is being blown up, but they will not move with respect to the balloon surface. Analogically, that surface is space and the dots are galaxies; the motions we observe correspond to an inflating of the balloon and give us what the astronomers call our expanding universe. Incidentally, we can see how recessional speeds even greater than the speed of light might be reconciled with that speed's being a limit on the motion of any matter; locally, with respect to the space, there would not be greater-than-light speeds for any galaxy.

When we speak of a cosmological model we refer to the total space-plus-galaxies, with possibilities for expansion (or contraction) of the space. The space of the model must be *all* of the space in the universe. It was Einstein who first proposed in our times the liberating idea of a universe which is both finite and yet without physical boundaries, with firm mathematical support for this notion from his relativity theory of gravitation. Again, we can illustrate a finite universe, which yet nowhere comes to an end, by means of a spherical surface. If such a two-dimensional surface is taken as being the entirety of space, we have a domain which is finite but also has no boundaries. To an insect, for example, living on the surface of an orange and able neither to penetrate below the surface or fly into the surrounding space, the orange's surface might be the entire conceivable universe. Still, it would be a finite universe, even though without boundaries. Likewise, Einstein proposed that the physical three-dimensional space of our experience is finite in extent; that it curves "back upon itself" rather than at any place coming to an end. Admittedly, the notion is not an easy one to grasp. Mathematically, the Einstein equations show that in such a finite, curved-space universe the amount of space included within a sphere of radius R, drawn about a given point, would at first increase with increase of R. But as R is extended, the volume included would eventually reach a maximum and then begin to decrease with continued growth of R. Finally, with a sufficiently large R, the enclosed volume would come to zero; one must conclude that a motion along the radius R has brought one back to one's starting point.

The relativity theory equations lead to explicit relations between, on the one hand, the extent of the universe and its degree of curvature, and, on the other hand, the observed density and distribution of galaxies and their motion of expansion. Hence, using the present theory, we can see the possibility of learning what actually is the correct cosmological model. In practice, the required observations are difficult to obtain and to interpret. Also, the theory allows wide latitude in the possible models. Thus, curvature may be "negative," with space opening up with distance like a tuba horn rather than closing as a sphere, and hence giving an infinite universe; or space may be Euclidean ("flat") and infinite. The present expansion may go on forever, or it may be followed by a period of contraction of space, with perhaps an unending series of such grand oscillations, each many tens of billions of years in temporal extension.

Also, there is always the possibility that modifications in the basic theory may be found to be necessary. Currently, the recently discovered quasars and pulsars add puzzling features which do not fit into what has been established in astrophysics about stellar bodies. Quasars are observed objects which appear both to be very distant, because they have a large red-shift in their spectra, and of enormous magnitude compared with a star; and yet they seem to be single, coherent bodies, rather than collections of stars as in a galaxy. It may be that the quasars show us astronomical objects which were formed in an epoch at an early stage of the expansion of the universe but which do not persist into the present epoch (and hence are not seen in the spatial regions lying relatively close to our galaxy). Pulsars are bodies that strongly emit radiations, in the radio-wave rather than visible range of the spectrum; and the radiation is characterized by well-defined intensity oscillations ("pulses"), with a pulse frequency of the order of one per second. For some pulsars the frequency has been observed to be slowly changing with time. Pulsars, although highly interesting objects, may not be so significant cosmologically as quasars. They are not enormous, as are the latter, and they apparently are within our galaxy, which quasars certainly are not if their red-shift is a correct indication of their distance. Pulsars are believed to be "neutron stars": small, highly condensed bodies, with very rapid axial rotation of the same frequency as the emitted pulses, and with magnetic fields which are responsible for the radiation emission. Some speculation to the effect that quasars and pulsars are related bodies has been put forth. In any event, we clearly have much to learn about both, and we should in general be prepared for surprising developments when we are at so early a stage in scientific cosmological studies.

Still, we could say that the current evidence and theory rather strongly support the idea that the universe has come to the state we now observe from earlier highly condensed states. That is, the universe is in this way cosmologically "evolutionary." Whether it is finite or infinite in total extent is at present an open question, although perhaps all factors together, both observational and theoretical, would give a bit more weight on the side of its being finite with positive (closed) curvature. With regard to its total history in time, the most satisfactory conception theoretically is that of the oscillating universe, and the direct evidence is no more favorable for any other model. Such a universe, finite and closed, would require no single creation event, and indeed could be regarded as timeless in its large-scale features, since any one grand cycle of expansion and contraction would be the same as any other; progressive, onward moving time would exist only in association with the developments within any one cycle. The oscillating model, too, gives to the universe the over-all property of being in a steady state, in that no one type of change, as expansion or contraction, would continue forever in a given direction.

An oscillating universe would not, however, require a continuous, spontaneous creation of matter, as well as continual expansion: these are features of a particular steady-state model that was postulated in 1948 by the British astrophysicists, Fred Hoyle, Hermann Bondi, and Thomas Gold. In their very challenging and interesting model the large-scale density of matter remains constant in any observable universe, the loss of matter by passage "over the horizon" in the expanding universe being compensated by spontaneous formation of new matter in space. The proposed creation rate is only about one hydrogen atom per liter of space per billion years; but this rate is large enough to provide the matter, eventually collected into great clouds of particles and then finally into galaxies, that would maintain on the cosmic scale a constant galactic density. However, the theory seems now, at least in its form as initially suggested, to be untenable. The quasars tentatively give evidence for an earlier state in which the universe had different large-scale features than it does today, and such a difference is counter to the postulated steady-state universe. Also, in the past few years a uniformly distributed electromagnetic radiation has been discovered which has just the properties that are to be expected of residual radiation from an earlier and much condensed state of the universe; again, such a state should not have ever occurred, according to the Bondi-Gold-Hoyle theory. Theoretically, too, the model suffers from a contradiction, since creation of matter everywhere at a uniform rate is calculated, if carried on through an actual *infinity* of past time, to lead to a physically impossible matter density (even in a spatially infinite universe).

We might think of cosmology as being in the same relative stage of completeness as was our knowledge of Earth's surface at the time of the later Greek geographers or, perhaps, as was our conception of the solar system at the time of Tycho Brahe. Of course, it would be presumptuous to assume that we shall in cosmology have the same eventual success that we have had with respect to Earth and the planetary system of which it is a part. But we have seen that a beginning has been made, with use of the observational techniques and theoretical methods of physical science. If progress continues in the next ten decades, say, as it has in the past five, science may well have brought us to the establishment of the correct cosmological model.

However, the prize that we are here seeking is one of the greatest that can be envisioned, and the possibility should not be discounted that we will find the goal unattainable. The natural world may have characteristics that limit our cosmological knowledge. On the microscopic level there is a limit, we saw, but one that is not unsatisfying, since the structure of nature itself seems to lose definiteness as we try to push precise space-time description to very small magnitudes. But perhaps on the cosmological scale we will find that vastness simply extends beyond the range of transmission of signals which might carry information; that, for example, an infinite universe is indicated as being the correct inference from theory and observation, but that its universal expansion prevents our learning about it beyond a certain observable limit. We would then have to be resigned to knowing only our "observable universe"—which would, of course, still be incredibly vast; and, even the definite knowledge of an infinite property would be a great achievement. Or, we may find that the universe is inhomogeneous in large-scale structure, in a way that makes cosmological characterization virtually hopeless. So far, cosmologists have generally assumed a uniformity in large-scale structure, and this assumption has been fairly well borne out; the density of galaxies in space, for example, seems not to vary with direction of observation. It is not easy to conceive of a situation in which we could not hope to discern some over-all regularity in description, but we must not prejudge what will be found.

Currently cosmology is an active science, with new factual data steadily coming in and with what plausibly is an adequate theoretical framework for interpretation and guidance of observations. Further, there is as yet no indication of insurmountable barriers to determination of the correct cosmological model. The present time is, indeed, perhaps a golden period in cosmology. Until we are forced to think otherwise there is, then, no reason to doubt that it is within man's power to comprehend the structure of the total astronomical universe. We have steadily pushed outward the range of our orientation in space and time, and science may well have the ability to go the whole way. If a limitation does appear, it will be, it would seem, from what is in nature itself: that it may be the way of the world that information necessary for characterization of its entirety cannot be attained at any one point-like region in space and time. But if this condition is so, the very establishment of it and of the details of its limitations will be a kind of fulfillment for cosmology.

6

SCIENTIFIC EXPLANATION

We ask more from science than descriptive accounts of
the natural world. We also want explanation: answers to
questions of "Why?" or "For what reason?" There is no
clear general principle about what will give satisfaction
as an explanation. Frequently, simple identification of
cause is sufficient. We return from a holiday and find a tree
near our home to be down; the explanatory statement that
there were high winds on a certain day will probably
suffice. Or, just knowing that an event is not unique may
be enough, as when a man has an illness with unusual
symptoms, and then is satisfied to be confidently told by
his doctor that it is some named disease (and, of course,
it is oddly reassuring if "it's been turning up everywhere
in this town").

But in science we usually mean by explanation the call-
ing up of a physical law or a principle of structure. In this
way we relate what we wish to explain to the general behavior of nature. We explain lightning, for example, by
bringing in the electronic structure of matter and the laws
of electrical charges: air movements give rise to frictional
accumulation of electrical charge and these are discharged
from cloud to cloud, or cloud to earth; we can, if we like,
even talk about the magnitudes of current and energy that
are involved. The closely related converse of this kind of
explanation is prediction in science. Applying the general
law we can predict the course of development of a given
set of circumstances. It is in this predictive property, of
course, that science is notably impressive in technology.

Thus the arrangements that will give an electric motor, a
steam turbine, or a nuclear reactor are successfully designed on the basis of the laws, respectively, of electro-
magnetism, thermodynamics, and nuclear physics.

In discussing the structure of science in Chapter 2, we
saw that there is a deductive as well as a descriptive aspect
of a well-developed science. It is this deductive property
that is of key importance in scientific explanation. By
means of it, we are able to see phenomena of a wide variety
as exemplifications of a general principle; or, as is sometimes said, we *subsume* all the instances in a given domain
under a general law that covers the domain. We have already discussed the science of mechanics as a prime example of a deductive science. Its basic laws give the principles in terms of which we can understand a very broad
range of mechanical behavior. Why does a wheel fly apart
if rotated sufficiently rapidly? We feel we explain when we
can show how the centrifugal force that causes the destruc-
tion is a consequence of Newton's laws of motion applied
to a rotating body.

In every field of science there is an attempt to do what
has been done in mechanics: to bring the myriad phenomena that are studied into a statement of a small number of principles. And, especially in the physical sciences,
there has been considerable success. It is true that scientists—even theoretical physicists—do not usually formalize
their deductive system into the same kind of rigorous
logical system of explicitly stated axioms and theorems
that is characteristic of a formal mathematical science.
Rather, they are content to establish general laws or equations and to relate these to others that are accepted as
established. To the extent that a natural science has a
logical structure it may be characterized as being *latently*
deductive rather than explicitly so. Thus a typical textbook
on mechanics will not contain the demonstration of a general theorem (principle) followed by deductive application
to all the known special situations. There may, in fact, be
very little discussion of applications if the book is one concerned with setting forth the general, abstract principles

of the science. Or, on the other hand, a textbook may simply state principles as something to have been learned or taken for granted from elsewhere, and proceed to apply them to a group of particular phenomena. In its rather loose deductive form, natural science retains flexibility for application to the wide variety of situations that may be of interest.

If all the aspects and details of nature which are studied in a given field of science can be seen as consequences of the general principles of the science, the science has then achieved a high degree of explanatory success. We saw earlier, in Chapter 3, that a science may be regarded as descriptively complete when as much detail as is desired has been obtained. We may now add to that criterion one for explanatory power, and thus come to a full statement for completeness in science: *a science is complete when it gives as much descriptive detail as is desired for the domain of the science and when the theoretical structure of the science satisfactorily explains all of the facts of the science.*

We could indeed say that completeness, as defined, has been reached for many restricted fields of science. For various kinds of mechanical phenomena, as already suggested, we can speak of a completed science. In another domain, we may cite the science of geometrical optics, which gives in a few principles the explanation of how light rays behave in any system of lenses and mirrors. A few laws of chemical combination constitute the principles in terms of which we understand hosts of different chemical compounds. The science of genetics explains quite rationally at least the statistical distribution of inherited characteristics. Every scientist could probably propose fields of science— if allowed to be sufficiently restricted—which have been virtually completed (but always too, probably, with a reservation about the principles used not themselves being satisfactorily understood).

Suppose we think, however, not of individual scientific fields, but of science as a whole; can we still hold for science a goal of complete explanation/ There has been impressive progress, in the development of science, in the bringing of widely different phenomena under one set of principles. A celebrated example occurred in the nineteenth century. The behavior of light as a wave with certain properties had been established in optics, and many different aspects of electrical and magnetic phenomena had been satisfactorily formulated mathematically. The British physicist James Clerk Maxwell beautifully brought together these studies, which had been independent, by showing that light was a particular kind of electromagnetic wave. In our century we have seen, for example, the variations in chemical properties of the elements explained as a consequence of the electronic configurations of atoms as elucidated in research on atomic structure. A significant uniting of chemistry and physics under one explanatory principle was thereby achieved. Currently, much of biology is coming to be understood in terms of physical-chemical processes, with explication of such details as, for example, the contraction of a muscle; or, understanding comes through the establishing of molecular structures, as of the double helix which allows both the replication and information carrying that are basic in reproduction of biological organisms.

There is in the philosophy of science a doctrine known as *reductionism*. Its proponents argue that eventually all of the processes of nature will be shown to be physical processes; or, in an alternative statement, that all of the natural sciences will eventually be found to be subsumed under the principles of physics. There is a substantial amount of evidence which the reductionist can marshal in support of his case. We have already mentioned an important instance of the explanation of chemical behavior in terms of basic physical structure, and many more could be given. Progress in understanding the functioning of biological organisms has in large part been by discerning the physical-chemical mechanisms that are involved: the formation and dissolution of a weak chemical bond between oxygen and blood hemoglobin, for example,

1. The science of the twentieth century surpasses that of any previous age, both in its content and as a basis for further discovery. An illustration such as this photograph of the Pleiades, in the constellation Taurus, suggests the boundlessness of the universe. The medieval concept of a limited heavenly canopy is represented in this sixteenth-century woodcut, depicting the new world view of Nicholas of Cusa. His concept has been definitely refuted by astronomical observation. (Photo courtesy of Deutsche Verlags-Anstalt.)

2. Electrons moving through a magnetic field trace a circular path, as shown in this photograph. The charge and mass properties of the electron may be inferred from observation of such paths, even though we cannot see the electron itself. The visible path results from vapor condensing on charged atoms (ions) that are formed in a gas as a kind of wake behind energetically moving electrons. (Photo courtesy of Professor Ernst Brüche.)

3. A technique for photographically registering the emission of electrons from atoms makes it possible to display the positions of individual atoms in a crystalline substance. In this micrograph, made by J. J. Hren and R. A. Neuman of the University of Florida, each bright spot represents an individual tungsten atom; the dark jagged line running across the photograph indicates a boundary between two tungsten crystals. (Photo courtesy of J. J. Hren and R. A. Neuman.)

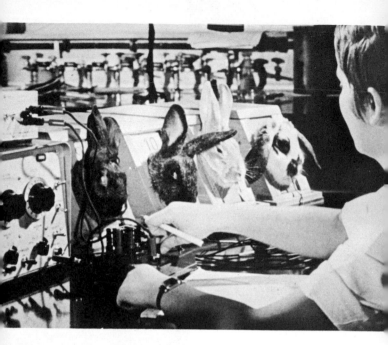

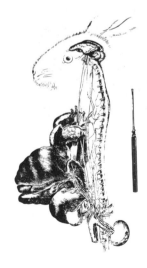

4. (*Opposite page and left*) The same animal presents varied aspects, each of which may seem central to a particular kind of person. Thus, the ecologist or conservation officer, the zoologist interested in animal morphology, the child concerned with his pet, the physiologist concerned with reproduction, the microbiologist requiring a test animal, and the biochemist studying carbohydrate metabolism each selects for study elements of the total organism, rabbit. (Photos courtesy of Deutsche Verlags-Anstalt.)

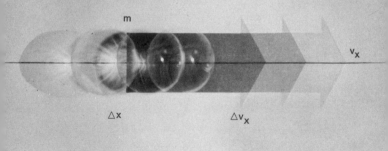

$p_x = m \cdot \Delta v_x$

m

v_x

Δx Δv_x

5. A representation of the uncertainty relation. For any dimension x there are intrinsic uncertainties for an atomic particle: Δx in the position and Δv_x in the velocity. The product of the uncertainties $\Delta x \cdot \Delta p_x$ must at least equal Planck's constant, h. ($\Delta p_x = m \cdot \Delta v_x$, where m is the mass of the particle and v_x is the velocity in the x direction.) (Photo courtesy of Deutsche Verlags-Anstalt.)

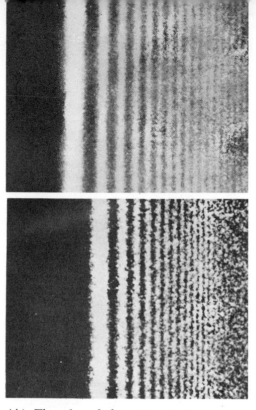

6. (A) The edge of the screen creates a source of light waves, with the result that instead of a sharp black shadow line we find a region of light and dark bands that merges into the region of uniform light illumination. At the light bands the waves come "in step" from the edge; the slight differences in distance of travel put them "out of step" at the dark bands, so that wave crest is canceled by wave trough. (Reproduced from Valasek © 1949, *Introduction to Theoretical and Experimental Optics.* Reprinted by permission of John Wiley & Sons.)

(B) We have here the same phenomenon as in A, but for electrons rather than light; hence we see a vivid illustration of the wave nature of electrons as they move through space. The wavelength λ of the moving electron is inversely proportional to its velocity v, and is given by the De Broglie equation, $\lambda = h/mv$, where m is the electron mass. (Reproduced from H. Raether, "Elektroninterferenzen," *Encyclopedia of Physics*, Vol. 32, Springer Verlag, Berlin, 1957.)

7. Greek sculpture: Head of Athena. Greek art combines a direct realism with ideals of beauty and coherence; harmoniously, in Greek thought there is fusion of wide study of nature with logic and deep ethical-religious concern. (Reproduced courtesy of Helmut Weygandt.)

8. Canaletto (Giovanni Antonio Canal) 1697–1768: *The Upper Reaches of the Grand Canal*. In this eighteenth-century painting there are tacit assumptions similar to those of eighteenth-century Newtonian science: the world is disposed in an orderly, definite manner, and there is emphasis on its extension in a geometric (Euclidean), three-dimensional space. (Reproduced courtesy of the Trustees of The National Gallery, London.)

9. Giacomo Balla 1871–1958: *Dog on a Leash*. In this Futurist painting (1912) we see a parallel with the Heisenberg Uncertainty Principle (1926): the motion of the dog's legs is displayed by giving a set of different positions to each leg, whereas the Uncertainty Principle asserts that there is not any precise position of an atomic particle. In both painting and Principle we have the natural world not as completely determinate but as dynamic and undefined in many of its properties. (Reproduced courtesy of George F. Goodyear and the Buffalo Fine Arts Academy, Buffalo, New York.)

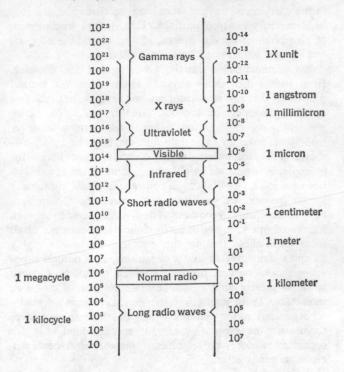

Frequency, cycles/sec		Wavelength, meters	
10^{23}			
10^{22}		10^{-14}	
10^{21}	Gamma rays	10^{-13}	1X unit
10^{20}		10^{-12}	
10^{19}		10^{-11}	
10^{18}		10^{-10}	1 angstrom
10^{17}	X rays	10^{-9}	1 millimicron
10^{16}		10^{-8}	
10^{15}	Ultraviolet	10^{-7}	
10^{14}	Visible	10^{-6}	1 micron
10^{13}		10^{-5}	
10^{12}	Infrared	10^{-4}	
10^{11}		10^{-3}	
10^{10}	Short radio waves	10^{-2}	1 centimeter
10^{9}		10^{-1}	
10^{8}		1	1 meter
10^{7}		10^{1}	
10^{6}		10^{2}	
1 megacycle 10^{6}	Normal radio	10^{3}	1 kilometer
10^{5}		10^{4}	
10^{4}		10^{5}	
1 kilocycle 10^{3}	Long radio waves	10^{6}	
10^{2}		10^{7}	
10			

FIGURE 12 Electromagnetic spectrum. James Clerk Maxwell showed that light consists of electromagnetic waves (jointly oscillating electrical and magnetic fields). These waves all travel in empty space with the "speed of light," 186,000 miles/second or 3×10^8 meters/second. The chart shows the waves, of widely differing wavelengths, that make up the electromagnetic spectrum. Those that are visible, which we see as light, constitute only a small portion of the total spectrum.

in the carrying of oxygen from lungs to tissue; or, the role of electrically charged particles, ions, in the transmission of signals along nerves. Indeed, almost the whole of modern biology would constitute illustrations in point.

But arguments too can be given against the doctrine. Even within the purely physical realm there are natural properties that are significant on one level of organization but then disappear on another. Nuclear forces, for example, which are all-important between the protons and neutrons that make up an atomic nucleus, have no role whatsoever over somewhat larger distances, not even, for example, between two neighboring atoms in the crystal lattice of a solid. Gravitation, in contrast, is trivial in intensity within the nucleus, or between the electrons and nucleus of an atom, but becomes a dominating force between masses of many, many billions of atoms. It does not at all seem implausible that in the organization of the highly complex structures of living organisms, new natural properties should appear, properties which cannot be reduced to those present among non-animate systems of atoms or molecules. There might be characteristic forces or modes of organization for systems which are able to reproduce themselves; or properties of still another kind only for organisms which have significant memory and conceptualization capabilities.

Biologists in our day have tended to be skeptical about admitting the existence of any kind of biological mechanism that is not ultimately reducible in understanding to physical-chemical description; for so much of the advancement of their science has resulted from looking for just that kind of explanation. I shall not here attempt to make any inexpert judgments about the correctness or error of reductionism. The developments in science must themselves show us the extent to which physics can provide complete explanation in science.

But in any event there is in prospect increasing coordination of the sciences, so that, even though factual, descriptive knowledge rapidly grows, there is also growth of the theoretical structure which organizes the facts. A few physical-chemical principles can now explain—or gen-

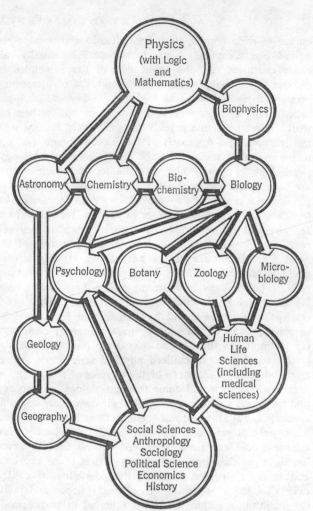

FIGURE 13 A chart of dependency relationships among the sciences; the arrows indicate "contributions to." According to the *reductionist* thesis the theoretical structures of all the sciences are reducible ultimately to the principles of basic physical science. In a counter point of view it is maintained that *emergent* independent principles appear in sciences with the increasing complexity of their objects of study.

eralize—a wide domain of special situations that once required two completely separate sciences. Essentially, already centuries ago, the application of the principles of physics to the material bodies and radiation of astronomy brought these two sciences together. Today the biologist must study biochemistry and biophysics to further his work; many academic psychologists do their science with the methods and approach of the biologist; and perhaps tomorrow the social scientist will consider biology-psychology to provide him with the set of principles that are basic to his science. Even if there is not a reduction to physics, we can justifiably look forward to increasing integration and explanatory power in science. We might foresee an ideal future structure: a master explanatory science, stating principles that describe the behavior of the most general features of the natural world; this science could be expected to be a development from present-day physics, but perhaps with, among others, new factors coming from biology, psychology, and cosmology. Then, various special sciences would have their own first principles as consequences of the general master science: chemistry, for example, as the science of matter on the molecular level, and also the specialized physical sciences of astronomy and geology. Going to higher degrees of complexity of organization, we would come through biology, psychology, and the social sciences, each with their own many scientific specialties, but always consequent in their basic ideas from more general sciences. The projected virtually complete science would explain any desired natural fact, by showing through what property of nature it is to be expected, and would also give mankind the possibility of control over all matters of health, environment, social and political institutions within the limits inherent in nature itself.

The optimistic future that I have suggested for science is reminiscent of an earlier time, when there were many who saw in science the answers to all of mankind's problems. The present-day military activities, problems of overpopulation, and hazards of industrialization do not show that confidence to have been entirely justified. Yet we should by no means dismiss it as altogether unfounded. Science has immensely improved the lot of mankind; and in its firm knowledge it has given us power and achievement that almost seem to be changing man into a species different from his pre-scientific predecessor. So we shall fully accept the achievement and continuing role of science. But there are important ways in which the explanatory power of science is not satisfactory as a complete philosophy of the natural world.

There is, first, the point to be made that because of the indeterminism that physics has found in nature on the microscopic level, there will be no explanation in science for why one individual quantum event occurs rather than another that may be equally probable. This limitation could be accepted as merely the consequence of an element of chance in nature. But in a more general way, it is associated with the breakdown of close space-time description for individual quantum events. With these, we come to an end of science as a rational ordering, just because the individual event cannot be known through any kind of predictive calculation but only through measurement. Indeed, as we have seen, the clear implication of the Superposition Principle of quantum mechanics is that the individual event is created, in one state out of a number of possible states, in the interaction-observation process. As we go to larger scale systems of many particles, the approximately deterministic, objective world of entities of space-time description becomes dominant; but on the quantum level *we must simply accept the being of individual events as they occur.* Hence, there is a kind of end to scientific explanation, on that level. This limit has not as yet bulked large in the significance of science, because our direct concern with individual quantum-scale events has been slight. Still, it is philosophically of major importance that we have come to a level of natural phenomena where, although not overlooking the regularities which do hold for ensembles of many events, we find for single events the irreducible assertion of being, beyond the net of any cognitive system. And consideration of individual atomic events may be found to be of significance for the course of many of the processes of life and thought in living organisms. Should this be found to be so, the quantum-level limit could well have profound implications for what we expect from scientific understanding and explanation.

There is a second limit on scientific explanation, one of powerful finality that is intrinsic to science. It exists in association with the deductive structure of science. This structure does give explanation, since it requires that specific instances follow from more general principles; but also, the deductive system rests on principles or axioms which are themselves simply to be accepted, and hence without explanation in the sense of being consequences of some other assertions of the system. The process of explaining nature by use of a deductive science comes to a halt with the first principles of the science. These may themselves be consequences of principles of some yet more general science, and so may be explained by those broader principles. But the explanatory procedure must eventually come to an end with the principles of the most general deductive science.

As an illustration, consider an incident of a broken dish being found on the floor in one's room. The first answer to "What happened?" may be simply the ascertaining of the details of the occurrence: that, say, apparently a woman dusting in the room unknowingly brushed the dish off a table. The investigation of why it broke when it struck the floor could take the line of asking about such matters as the crystalline structure of the dish and the precise manner in which it was jarred on stopping. But let us take the simpler course of saying that it broke because it fell, and that it is a property of heavier-than-air objects to drop toward the earth when unsupported. Our explanation of this propensity can be in terms of gravity, and we can in turn refer this to the law of Newton, which tells us that between any two bodies there is a gravitational force proportional to the product of their masses and to the inverse square of the distance between them. Until about fifty years ago this would have been the end of our explanatory process. But now we can see Newton's law of gravity as a special case of the more general equations of Einstein, which show gravitational force to arise as a space-time curvature that is associated with matter and energy. We might want still further to ask, "But why do matter and space-time curvature go together?" However, in the present state of physics we can go no further, and must be gratefully content with the generality of explanation that has been achieved.

The basic equations and terms of electromagnetic theory constitute a set of explanatory principles, for a wide range of phenomena, for which there is no explanation by reference to yet more general equations. It was the hope of Albert Einstein that he could find a fundamental theory of the physical field which would have as consequences both the gravitational and the electromagnetic equations, and, indeed, also the equations that describe the elementary particles of nature and their unique interaction forces. So far, it does not appear that the equations which he proposed, late in his life, are capable of doing what he hoped to achieve. Still, physicists will continue to work toward greater unification of the deductive systems in the various sub-fields of physics.

The earlier limitation on explanation that we discussed, arising from the role of measurement-interaction itself in forming quantum-magnitude events, suggests that a complete master theory is not possible. But also for any theory that is developed, we will have the limitation that comes with the underived, unexplained principles which are at the base of the theory. Science progressively has given us further explanation and understanding of nature, even though at certain places, notably in quantum physics, nature herself has set end points. Over-all, there is no reason to expect that these riches of science will not continue to grow. Always, however, the explanation comes to a stopping place, where one must extend science if one would know more. This never-finished quality of science seems to give it the virtue of being adequate to the unfathomed extent of our natural world. Also, though, it gives science the property that always there are last questions for which there are no answers. Just as in any other cosmology we can ask, "But who made the gods?" The possible reply, that you have failed in your religion if you must press this question, is one that we shall come to in the final chapter.

There is one more aspect of deductive systems and explanation which I want briefly to discuss. It concerns a mathematical principle, known as Gödel's Theorem, which, in addition to its great influence in mathematical thinking, has been widely discussed in philosophical circles.

We want, of course, that a deductive system be consistent within itself. This means that nowhere in the system are there statements which are contradictory with respect to some relationship or attribute.* In natural science the appearance of a contradiction, either as a result of new observations or from mathematical investigations, is a sign of something seriously wrong and can often lead to basic reconstruction in theoretical structure. Thus the result of the celebrated Michelson-Morley experiment, that the speed of light shows no effect from relative motion of source and observer with respect to the presumed ether, contradicted the assumption that light has a constant speed

---

* It is an interesting property of a deductive system that if it contains even a single contradictory statement then *any* statement which can be made with the terms or symbols of the system can be proven in the system. It is easy to see why this is so. Suppose the inconsistency to be in the two assertions, "A is true" and "A is false." Let B be any other statement. Now, from "A is true," it follows that either: i) A is true and B is false; or ii) A is true and B is true. But it has been asserted that A is false, so we do not have i). Hence we have ii), which asserts that B is true. There is a story that the great Cambridge mathematician, G. H. Hardy, once commented in a college dinner conversation that if $2 + 2 = 5$ then any other statement can be proved. To the challenge of a table companion, "Prove that I am the Pope," Hardy replied, "By subtraction of 3 we get $1 = 2$, and hence you and the Pope, two, are identically you, one."

with respect to the ether. Similar unexpected observations (along with conjugate theoretical considerations) led to Einstein's foundation work in the theory of relativity.

For a mathematical-logical system that is consistent (and there is not likely to be much interest in one that is not) it had since Greek times been assumed that any proposition asserted in the terms of the system could in principle be either proven or disproven, i.e., could either be shown to follow or not to follow from the axioms of the system. Gödel, however, in 1931 demonstrated that it is possible, if a system is consistent, to formulate propositions in it which are *undecidable,* that is, which can neither be proven nor disproven. He showed this for any deductive system which is sufficiently complex to contain the content of ordinary arithmetic; further, his ingenious construction whereby one can formulate statements about provability in a mathematical system insured that the undecidable statements are themselves mathematical propositions (e.g., of arithmetic).

The Gödelian statements are exemplifications of a basic logical property of deductive systems. As such, they are not primarily content-statements, and to date Gödelian sentences have not been found which express undecidable properties that are of specific mathematical interest. Still, there is no reason why they may not be. But the great import of the theorem has been in the new way it has forced mathematicians to regard the proof possibilities of a deductive system. The pre-Gödelian view assumed a rigorous completeness for such a system, within its own compass. But now we know that even with the most stringent care in setting up a deductive system, we cannot insure that every proposition of the system will be demonstrably true or false; there will inevitably be those with the status of Gödelian undecidability. In his work, Gödel showed that by going to a *meta-system* which encompasses a system, in a manner such that in the new system one can talk about the original system, the undecidability can be removed in that original system. But one gains at a price, for in the

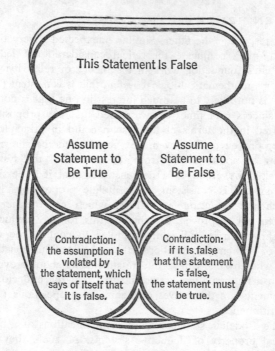

FIGURE 14 In language self-reference can lead to paradox, as illustrated by the above "Paradox of the Liar." Kurt Gödel showed that in a logically consistent mathematical system there are propositions, with self-reference similar to that of the Liar Paradox, which are undecidable and cannot be either proven or disproven within the system.

new system undecidable propositions can again be formulated, and so on.

The theoretical systems of physics do most certainly contain arithmetic, and one readily wonders if there may therefore be undecidable Gödelian assertions about the physical world. In fact, no one has constructed a Gödelian sentence with direct relevance for physics, or for any other natural science. And if one were formulated, it might be expected that the undecidability could be removed by appeal outside the system, that is, to the natural realm which is the concern of the science.

There is, however, an interesting parallel between Gödel's Theorem and limitations that we have noted in scientific description. In their verbal interpretation, Gödel's undecidable mathematical propositions are, as we have noted, statements which talk about their own provability. We have a similar kind of ordinary language assertion in the "paradox of the liar." If I say, "This statement is false," my assertion is neither consistently true nor false: if true, it is false by its content; if false, it is true, since it is then false that it is false. By virtue of its *self-reference*, the sentence is undecidable. In a somewhat similar way,

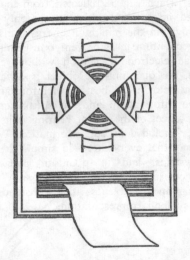

FIGURE 15 There is a simple, logical limitation on any descriptive process when we consider self-description. A hypothetical "describing machine" might be devised to report on varied aspects of the world, but it could not make a report on its own activity. A statement, "This machine is now not active," would be false, as the machine made it.

the Gödelian proposition is undecidable in a consistent deductive system.

Now we saw that in a very simple, direct way self-reference carries with it a limitation on description: the "descriptive machine" (Chapter 3), cannot describe its own inactivity. We can likewise see a self-reference in the limitation on quantum-level description. We learn of the state of an electron or a photon, for example, by the energy effect it has in the interaction-observation that brings it into that state. There are limitations in this knowledge: thus, the particle cannot (Uncertainty Principle relations) tell us precisely of its position state when the apparatus is designed to have it tell us of its momentum state. For a large-scale object there are smaller particles, e.g., photons, which can be reflected from the object and bring detailed information which refers only to the undisturbed body, but the minimum energy-transfer interactions on the quantum level prevent our gaining information about an electron or photon without changing its state. Hence, the quantum-size object is always to some extent both a factor in the bearing of information and the object of the information; and, to speak somewhat figuratively, the effect of the act of bearing is itself a factor not altogether included in our information. We can generalize and say that everywhere—in simple description, in deductive systems, and in quantum phenomena—self-reference places limitations on knowledge. We see again that Being has an assertiveness that withstands any effort at complete symbolic representation.

7

SCIENCE AND THE HUMANITIES

A listing of characteristic traits would probably not disclose any profound difference between scientific and humanistic activities. In each there must be imagination, devotion, observation, reasoning, with discipline and training in certain canonical forms of procedure and expression. The relative amounts of these ingredients will vary, but that is true from science to science, or art to art, as well as between the sciences and the arts. And yet we are not likely to think that science achieves much the same thing as does work in the humanities. I shall try to elucidate the difference that does exist, and thereby hope also to make explicit certain of the bounds of science.

By the humanities I shall mean the entire range of activities in which men set forth, through some medium of expression, responses to various aspects of our world, but without striving for the non-personal content and the rigorously defined language that are characteristic of science. So, I take the humanities to mean the various fine arts, and also music, poetry, fiction, criticism, theater, philosophy, and theology. Of course, in some of their manifestations these activities may be primarily utilitarian; or, again, they may become essentially scientific, as in parts of academic philosophy, or in "humanistic scholarship" which is primarily an effort toward historical description. History itself, although certainly not without elements of the characteristic approach of the humanist, seems best to be thought of as one of the social sciences.

Centrally, the humanist gives us a vivid insight: perhaps for a concrete scene, as in the selection made by a (realistic) painter; or, in what effect circumstances may have in the course of a life, as conceived by a novelist; on the highest level of generality, the humanist may be a philosopher-theologian who elucidates a possible significance of a way of living.

Of course, science too gives us insights. But the humanist can depict, and convey, that which has been excluded from the concern of the scientist. We have discussed in Chapter 3 the descriptive limitations on science; there is no attempt to present every fact about nature, but usually only those which have wide significance in the description of an element or domain of the natural world. Further, there certainly is no interest in what particular attitude the scientist has toward that which he is studying. A statement by a physicist, for example, that he found a crystal whose infrared absorption properties he was measuring to have an appearance that gives him nostalgic memories of a boyhood toy would hardly be acceptable in a scientific paper. But full concentration on a particularity and on a unique human response is often the very essence of a work of art.

A kind of fruit—an apple, for example—may be exhaustively described in a scientific treatise with respect to form and structure, conditions for growth, chemical composition, nutritional values, and so on. Yet, what it can mean to a person is by no means altogether contained in the scientific description. The appearance of a rosy apple with light reflecting from it in a certain way is a theme for a painter or photographer rather than botanist. Its joyful taste after a hot, dry walk or the sight of a laden apple orchard on an autumn afternoon can be elements that add a bit to a poem or story. It would seem that in general many of the richnesses and complexities that are a part of human experience would fail to be expressed if science were the only descriptive activity.

But just as the scientist has an interest in describing salient features of the universe, as delineated by some goal, intellectual or otherwise, the artist too must of course make a selection. He commonly does so on the basis of his own emotional responses. Further, in what he depicts he is free to emphasize and suppress as he wishes; the final result is usually understood to be his communication of a way of feeling about a bit of the universe, and only in part an objective description of that bit. In most of the arts today he may, in fact, devote his work primarily to his own emotion and thought, with slight content from the commonly recognized external world. In one art, that of instrumental music, we always expect very little in descriptive content; the composer carries his insight and emotion through the form and sensuous quality of sound.

The deficiency that descriptive science has, in not giving the richness of particularity and of individual human response, is perhaps its most obvious limitation. And, it is easy to see how art, broadly conceived, makes up this lack. The person who reads in literature, attends the theater, the cinema, and art exhibitions can widely supplement his experience in ways that would not come with even the most intensive study of natural science. Of course, we must indeed remember that the basic experience of what the world directly is to a human being comes from the actual surroundings and people of a person's own life. But literature and art can in a pleasurable way immensely extend that experience. More than that, they can give meaning to direct experience through contrast and relationship.

When we speak of art as doing more than vicariously extending experience, that is, when we think of its providing elements of significance and understanding, we clearly are referring to properties of the humanities that are somewhat akin to the theoretical, explanatory powers of science. We have seen, in the preceding chapter, that scientific explanation always comes to an end, because the deductive, theoretical structure of a science rests on first principles that are either taken as simply given, or, even if they may be consequences in a more general science, must themselves eventually lead back to a broader set of axiomatic principles. Inherently, then, deductive science can-

Photography, Realistic
Painting and Sculpture
Descriptive Writing

Theater, Fiction, Poetry

Ballet, Opera

Dance

Choral and Lyric Music

Abstract Painting
and Sculpture

Instrumental Music
Architecture
Design, Crafts

FIGURE 16 The arts vary widely in their descriptive content, as illustrated in the progression from the descriptive arts at the top of the sketch to the highly form-dominant ones at the bottom. But even in photography, for example, the artist contributes significant elements of selection and emphasis by which he conveys his insight or feeling.

not completely explain the universe. There is hence a role for the humanist to supply that which the scientist does not.

I do not mean that we should expect to find in the humanities those further extensions of science by which we can understand currently unexplained first principles in a given stage of science. Such extension is primarily the work of the scientist. (Although it is to be noted that a philosopher, or even an artist, may in his work sometimes point the way to a new approach in science. In his development of the physical interpretation of quantum mechanics Niels Bohr, for example, acknowledged an indebtedness to the philosopher William James.) But in two general ways the humanist supplements the scientist's truncated explanatory scheme. Humanists explore and influence our convictions in those realms where science has not set up its own rigorous and generally compelling results. And, secondly, we gain from the humanities a general outlook that is perhaps not so much one of understanding as one of acceptance of the universe. I want to discuss each of these two roles of the humanist in some detail and as it relates to results and beliefs from science.

We will start with the first role. The ways in which we behave and the things that we want from life are to a large extent determined by what we consider—in the ancient terms of Plato—to be the true, the good, and the beautiful. Our ideas about what is true have indeed been influenced, and now even largely determined, by the content and procedures of natural science. But conceptions of good and beauty, although obviously not unaffected by science, chiefly have their explication in the responses and insights of humanists. For the humanist it is not only the careful observation-deduction scheme of the scientist that is called into play, but the far wider realm of human experience and imagination generally.

For the time, I shall present only some considerations relating to questions of what is regarded as good in behavior. To a scientist it is noteworthy that the manner in which the humanities have their influence is highly unsystematic and even frequently inconsistent, in contrast with the way of the sciences. If a major problem is recognized in a science there will be a wide effort in the world's scientific community to solve it. Research workers will interest themselves in the problem and financial agencies may make specific funds available for support of work on it. Papers reporting results appear in the appropriate journals, usually with statements of the current status of the problem and recognition of the progress that has been made by others. Commonly the problem is eventually solved, or at least analyzed in some manner that is satisfactory. The conclusions find their way into treatises and textbooks; mankind's store of scientific knowledge has thus been improved. It does not appear that the humanist operates in any such even partially systematic way: beliefs and attitudes of a given time rarely are given the explicit codification of a treatise. And yet, there are movements in the arts, and there is dominance of an idea or point of view, as expressed in codes of behavior or in literature. A tendency toward a change in belief may be encouraged, for example, by a great artist, a key political figure, or a popular writer, who can be the major factor in the winning of people's minds to a specific concept of what is good.

The place of Jesus of Nazareth and his conception of Christian love readily comes to mind as an illustration of a single person deeply changing the ethical ideals of a large fraction of mankind. To illustrate with a more specific movement in human relationships, we might consider the sentiments in early and mid-nineteenth-century America that eventually led to the abolition of slavery in the United States. Many people of course participated in leading popular thought and action, but we can cite a novel, Harriet Beecher Stowe's *Uncle Tom's Cabin,* and the impact of a political leader, Abraham Lincoln, as being among the major influences. The arguments for abolition arose from many facets of human experience and with varied kinds of religious and philosophical support.

And, in spite of counter-arguments and social inertia, a conviction that involved a change in assumptions about human lives did eventually carry the day. New social-industrial factors may well have been, as some have argued, a factor in the challenge. The humanist, in any event, can be responsive to the *total* situation of his times. In the present day we still have a movement, in many other parts of the world as well as in America, for greater intrinsic mutual respect among people: in particular, for the disappearance of antagonism that is based simply on color or other racial traits. The whole wide spectrum of the humanists, from the artist to the theologian, is for the most part in support of this eradication of prejudice, much of which has deep roots in old traditions of superiority within a given set of people.

The scientist as such is not outside of general changes in point of view. In the matter of race prejudice, for example, the anthropologist has contributed in making clear what race differences are (and are not). And science, whose applications are the source of such problems as overpopulation and air-earth-water pollution, probably must also provide the techniques for their solution. But science exists in a matrix of human beliefs, wider than itself, that are shaped for any one person by tradition, religion, art, and literature, and with certainly a component from unique individual experience. These beliefs, which are crucial for the welfare of any one person and also for the success of society, are primarily in the domain of the humanist. Yet it would be a serious falsification to think of a neat compartmentalization, with the scientist giving us clear description and explanation, as far as he can go, while the humanist somewhat more emotionally proposes that we retain or modify, as the case may be, some given principle of life. In fact, science has been steadily encroaching during the past few hundred years on the humanist's domain—that is, we have seen many questions that once were subjects for the educated awareness of the humanist taken over by the objective procedures of the scientist

On a humble level, results from medical-biological studies have been substituted for many traditional beliefs with respect to ways of living; as a consequence we do (to some extent) behave and eat differently. On a more traditionally ethical level, our ideas about what is good and bad for children have, for example, tended to come rather more from psychologists and educators than from tradition or from religion. The adult who is in distress today may go to a psychiatrist; or, if to the church as in the past, he may very likely find his priest to have been influenced by efforts in the scientific studies of man. As we have earlier noted, the sciences have brought a basic naturalism into our views of human affairs; we look for causes and conditions in the natural or social world, rather than to divine will. In the growth of the social sciences there has been a widespread use of scientific methods for such problems as those of social change, of economic control, and of political organization.

There are people who deplore the growth of science and envision a grim day when all aspects of human life will be controlled by the unquestioned results of science. And, indeed, it is not hard to find instances where the growth of the realm of science has led to the substitution of the common for that of superior human quality or taste. But in all we must surely be deeply grateful for the removal of superstition and improvement in conditions of life that have come with science (even aside from the new knowledge and understanding that it has brought). With respect to the complete domination by science of human life, we must remember that at present the structure of science does by no means cover everything we do; even in this day of computers, we still plan our own holiday, and the novelist (or scientist) relies on his own approach and labor for the inspiration that yields a new insight. Secondly, there is the firm fact that the deductive structure of science does not itself explain its own first principles.

For this latter reason, even if men should find it desirable (as well they might) to use science in virtually all of the components of living, there would be an irreducible basis of belief that must be explained, if at all, outside of science. The computer might be used, for example, to decide which among alternatives would be the most satisfactory vacation trip, but it would have to be given information about what the activities are that bring pleasure to a particular person. Or the social scientist might be able to decide what are feasible possibilities in the planning of a new community, but there must be some broader decision about the qualities of life that are wanted in the community.

In sum, I do not think it is correct to assert, as is often done, that science is concerned only with techniques, and that how science is used is an altogether independent decision. The content of science has too much influence on what are the alternatives, and on our understanding of a given situation, to warrant such a complete separation. That is, science does affect the ends as well as provide the means: the avoidance of war, for example, is a matter of new urgency with the present possibilities for scientific warfare, and the position of pacifism therefore takes on heightened value as an end or goal. We can rather say that the interplay between science and traditional beliefs adds to the challenge to the humanities in our day. Science cannot primarily explain our first principles, because—to repeat again—it can justify the use of a set of principles but cannot explain them by reference to other principles. Even in the realm of the physical sciences there is, then, a role for an activity beyond that of science. And in the sciences which are directly concerned with human behavior, the humanist must have the responsibility of marshaling our basic beliefs: of discerning them, relating them among themselves, and of leading the way to adoption of the new and dropping of the old as the conditions of our world demand. Here too, as in the end point of individual quantum events in atomic physics, there is no rigorously rational, predictive scheme: we live out the drama of man, foreseeing and providing with reason as far as we can, but otherwise relying on what we trust is valid and sensitive response to the winds of change.

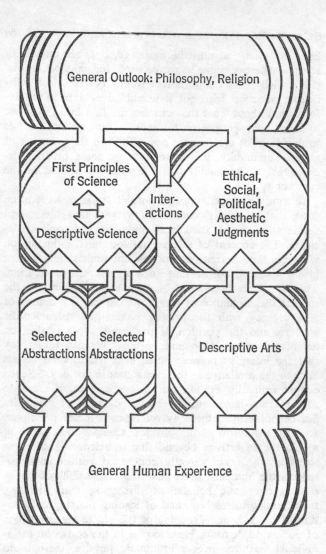

General Outlook: Philosophy, Religion

First Principles of Science ⟷ Descriptive Science

Inter-actions

Ethical, Social, Political, Aesthetic Judgments

Selected Abstractions   Selected Abstractions

Descriptive Arts

General Human Experience

The second role that I have suggested for the humanist in making up the shortcomings of the explanatory scheme of science is in the providing of a general outlook. We

FIGURE 17 The relationships among science and the other human activities that are concerned with knowledge, guidance, and understanding. There is a delimiting process in both columns coming up from general experience, with emphasis on intuition and unique personal response on the right, and on logical rigor and the other-than-human natural world on the left. But the differences are not exclusive and are only in emphasis. Hopefully, a harmonious general outlook that both elucidates and gains support from all activities is provided by religion and philosophy.

may hope that he can bring basic ideas, from the sciences and the humanities alike, into a unified conception of the universe. Further, we ideally expect of such a final doctrine that it will give us the kind of understanding that lends meaning to our lives.

In past centuries in the Western world the Christian religion has chiefly supplied the elements of an ultimate set of beliefs, and during the late medieval period there was that concordance of art, thought, and religious feeling which stands as a notable example of cultural unity. In architecture, in sculpture, in painting and tapestry, as well as in science, philosophy, religion, and social organization there were dominant elements of a common conception of man and of his universe. Christianity (far different, to be sure, in many of its practices and doctrines from the religion of today) was of course the unifying set of beliefs determining that common outlook. Dante's *Divine Comedy* is properly viewed as giving the culminating expression of Western medieval culture. Dante presented a detailed scientific description of the entire cosmos, as then conceived, and with a relating of the significance of individual acts in a person's life to the natural order of the universe—an interlocking that came with the cosmology developed in part on foundations in Christianity. Further, Dante harmoniously fits characteristic features of medieval life—romantic love, struggle between church and state, scholastic philosophy—into the God-centered world he describes.

For some people Christianity continues to be their bulwark of assurance against puzzlement and despair. It can hardly be denied, however, that the development of science has undermined the world outlook that was associated with Christian belief, and in many ways made the belief a less tenable one. For a large fraction of Western, educated people today the central tenets of Christianity have only historical significance, even though the ethical proposals of the religion may be accepted as valid ideals. Indeed, there are many grounds for arguing that the actually effective religion in the contemporary world is science itself. For, if religion is that which is looked to as the final authority, and as the source of aid in situations of pain and trouble, then for many, many persons science fits these conditions. "Science says" is commonly an unquestioned warrant for accepting a statement; reliance on established science, or the setting up of a research program, is often the response to an urgent problem. The successes of science constitute a considerable justification for the high place it has been given in the public regard, and I do not at all want to argue that we should substitute anything else for it, in its domain of competence. But we have seen that science does have inherent explanatory limitations. The aspects of experience which it describes are severely limited by the processes of selection of data that operate in each science; and, in the rather abstract scheme that is generally set up in a science for its domain of concern, the first principles or basic concepts are themselves without further explanation.

Taking as true the suggestion that today science does in fact function as a major religion, we can see some of the ills of our time as having their roots in science's inadequacies for that role. Certainly, a want of meaning for life, a lack of clear sense of human significance are often oppressive features in the lives of people who have otherwise achieved conditions for happiness. Or, to go to a problem of society, the persistence of war, for example, may be an indication of a political point of view that seems rarely to rise above selfish expediency in considering human welfare. In a word, it is an unfortunate fact that the world today seems to lack a religion that both is widely accepted by mind and heart *and* is adequate for the guidance of mankind.

A return to earlier, pre-scientific faiths can hardly be the solution to the present situation. Science, which is so much alive in our world, must form part of a viable religion: the corroboration of assertion through scientific investigation needs recognition as well as does the silent meditation in which men ask about their lives. There has been effort toward the achievement of a religion that does incorporate an encouragement for the scientific point of view. For one, the philosophy-religion identified as "humanism" has emerged: the high value of science in extending our knowledge of man and of the natural world is accepted, and at the same time the goals discerned as best for man in his various activities are encouraged. But the lack in religious humanism of a transcendent ultimate ground for explanation or reference has seemed to many to prevent its having the genuine power over thought and action of an effective religion.

In our day, the humanistic tradition as expressed in philosophy has not added much to a world view that takes its content largely from the results of science. The emphasis in philosophy, especially in England and in the United States, has been on analysis of meaning and the study of logical structure. In this work the goals have not at all been the formulation of a coherent synthesis that would bring together both the widely expanded and novel scientific knowledge which we now have and the principles that are more traditionally based in our human experience. Instead, the dominant analytic, logical, quasi-positivistic philosophy of our day has been rather ruthlessly examining criteria for validity or meaning, with the result that much of what was previously accepted as metaphysically secure has been demolished. One cannot be ungrateful for this critical movement in philosophy; as a consequence of it, there has been a development of rigor, with a tendency toward discouragement of personal bias. Philosophy—to some degree, no doubt, in imitation of science—has achieved greater freedom from the established outlook of a given social, religious, or political group. Such an increased objectivity is desirable indeed for the thought of our human species, which is of a single and common biological stock. Provincial, dogmatic doctrine can hardly be the mode by which we may come to terms with a natural universe wherein a particular verbal scheme, established only by authority and tradition, may have little relation to physical or biological reality.

And yet, we can also see that the analytic philosophy has tended to overemphasize man's scientific and logical responses to the universe. It is also possible to think about man as an organism that senses the universe in other than scientific ways and has requirements for his world which rest on those other modes of experience. Specifically, man has needs for broad concepts of his place and significance, and he has direct intuitions which are counter to statements, based on a narrow scientific discipline, which would reduce him to the humanly meaningless mechanisms of that discipline. The best traditions of philosophical thought have faced this inconsistency (Plato, for example, saw that the scientific conception of man did not explain his concern for justice), and today it gives rise to dilemmas for which we badly need philosophic resolutions. The fact that man as a natural being is moved by idealistic goals would seem to be ample warrant for the existence in nature of elements that have escaped the net of the special sciences.

But with acceptance of the pruning of belief or assumption that critical philosophical thought has now accomplished for the educated person, our hope for a more adequate religion must rest largely on the prospect of insights which are within the rigor we want in philosophical thought. Obviously, these insights must take into account the large share of the life of man that lies outside of scientific description. And they must carry their own explanation or conviction in a way that, we have seen, the axiomatic principles of science do not. A complete philosophy of this kind is hardly likely to be readily and totally forthcoming, but helpful partial insights are with us always. We can say, too, that it is part of the double role of science, as both destroyer of tradition and creator of new belief, that it also may contribute to a new synthesis, even with its own methods. For science does give us knowledge, and it may discern for man significance and value not at present evident in science as such.

We might again recall that, when the modern era of science had its beginning in Europe some five hundred years ago, the world was seen as a coherent unity, with final causes and ultimate purposes inhering in a God whose manifestations were everywhere apparent. That cosmos has now long been shattered by firm results of science. The resulting universe is comparatively open, is understood only in highly partial fragments, and is not obviously meaningful to man. But we cannot be certain of what the future may yet disclose: the men who laid the scientific foundations of the modern period, in the fourteenth and fifteenth centuries, surely did not expect that their work would lead to the discrediting of the Christian cosmos; likewise, we can say that it is possible that science may in the future find elements of meaning for man in nature that we do not see in the natural science of today. I do not want to deny what I have previously asserted: that the development of a satisfactory religion through science itself is virtually precluded by science's own structure. Very likely we must look to philosophers, theologians, and artists for our ultimate way of comprehending and taking the universe. But we can ask too, of these humanists, that they not neglect what science tells us: incomplete as it is, the new capability it gives to man has brought a profound change in the relationship he finds between himself and the universe.

I want finally to return to the relation of art and science. I have suggested that the artist in effect gives confrontations with the universe which generally would never come through science. But, in addition to having this role, does the artist also supplement the scientist on a more abstract level, as do the humanists—philosophers, critics, theologians—who contribute to our general beliefs and attitudes? That is, do we gain from the artist insights on the theory-explanation level as well as more concrete enrichments of knowledge and feeling? A suggestion that there is truth in art—and, indeed, perhaps even that it is only in art that we reach the supreme insights—is not uncommon. We should, if we accept this proposal, regard art and science as parallel efforts toward understanding.

There is, clearly, a common base in experience for science and art, and even some overlapping between the two in descriptions of nature. Thus, the scientist and the artist who are both attempting accurately to sketch a rare species of flower have skills in common. Generally, though, the element of personal selection and feeling in graphic art, especially now that photography can serve for accurate depiction, tends superficially to draw it away from science. Still, one can find striking similarities between the art and the science of a given historical period: a similarity in over-all characteristics which supports the idea that both show the influence of a common, basic way of looking at the world. The precision and formal grace of Greek art, for example, are akin to the coherent, rigorous Greek accomplishments in logic, mathematics, and philosophy (Photo 7). Eighteenth-century physics was reasonable, limited, and comprehensible; it does not seem farfetched to say that European composers and painters of that century depicted the world in a like manner (Photo 8). In our own times, the tidy world of Newtonian physics has become one that is relatively indeterministic, subjectivistic, vastly extended cosmologically, and highly abstract. These are characteristics that could well be ascribed to modern art—even the "cosmologically extended," as indicating a lack of sensible beginning or end in the world it portrays. One might argue that the radical late nineteenth-century and early twentieth-century painters anticipated the physicist in a break from the constraints of a more manifestly everyday world (Photo 9).

And yet I think it would be wrong to see art as primarily concerned with giving us insights about what the natural world is. Much of art work is devised for reasons of utility or of incidental decoration, and also much of music is for light entertainment of the moment; art for these purposes is hardly expected to be giving us profound and valid ideas about the universe. This fact is not itself conclusive; much of scientific activity, too, is utilitarian or trivial in respect to the general truths. But when we contrast major, serious works of art and of science, we find art to be directed to evocation of a feeling or an attitude, which may have direct external relation only to the art object or may be directed far beyond. There might be implicit truth about the natural world in what the artist wishes to convey, but certainly the method of giving conviction that science uses has not been employed; and there is an emphasis on feeling-response which is not central in science.

We might think, for example, of Vincent van Gogh's well-known painting of his bedroom at Arles. The rather sparse furnishings and humble bed suggest at once a simple life that must in this case be one of dedication by the painter to his work. The characteristic yellow colors convey the intensity of feeling that we associate with Van Gogh. But, in contrast to some of the later paintings, there is clarity, even serenity, in the life that is indicated by the well-arranged room. Also, obviously, there is loneliness. In sum, we may find in the painting both its own concrete, vivid attractiveness and a strong sense of a way of life, perhaps notably different from the viewer's or, alternatively, possibly by a kind of resonance giving a heightening to experiences of one's own self.

The artist's impact can of course range over all human experience. Staying still with Van Gogh, we recall his landscapes of cultivated fields in the neighborhood of Arles. Again, the intensity of the colors, the depiction of field plots and of farm equipment engender a feeling for what the earth is in southern France; indeed, one might say that the artist gives a somewhat concentrated essence of what one may experience from his surroundings in that region. One can of course readily multiply examples: John Constable's Stour valley landscapes, with the stream, woodland, meadow, and stone church tower telling us of English country life; or, the productive, rolling Iowa farmland which Grant Wood shows to us in his *Stone City*. But—and this is characteristic of art—a quality of the painting eludes us if we try to exhaust its role in a description of that which it tells the viewer. Seeing the painting is a non-verbal experience that may, if the painter is successful, be uniquely impressive as an enrichment of living.

With respect to understanding our world, I suggest that the contribution which the artist makes tends to be directed toward the conditions which man finds for life. These may simply be made more explicit by art, as when a painting does point up the feeling of what is present for man in a well-known country or city location; but also, properties of living that had not been realized may be brought to awareness in art. In this way the artist perhaps not so much creates as releases attitudes in those who read or look at or listen to his work. The artist is, presumably, a person of unusual awareness and sensitivity for the experiences of living, as well as one who by some medium of art can convey that which he thinks and feels. Hence his work can arouse feeling and thought that could be described as an emotion of pleasure, love, admiration, anger, aspiration—the list could go on almost indefinitely —with respect to some entity of experience.

Art, by its heightening of intensity of feeling through means that are outside a person's own self, may to some be that which makes life worth while. And by these effects art can come to be regarded as the source of what are the ultimate insights. There is a factor here, I would judge, of prizing direct experience with elements of living more highly than that which science can offer.

We should not forget that we live within a framework not of that which we choose but of that which is simply presented to us; the order and reasonableness that we can bring into our lives and natural world are bounded by given conditions: of birth and death, of the coming or disappearance of love and health and fortune, of the being of the world itself. Science, in the unexplained properties of its first principles and, recently, in the discerning of the irrational root events on the microscopic level, does come to barriers that have resemblances to these conditions. But art, in its own way, which is not that of the explicit, verbalized idea-construction of science, tells of the conditions. We can therefore gain experiences—of our emotions, of features of the world, of possibilities for life and for imagination—through the artist's perceptions. It seems not quite appropriate to say that an artist furthermore adds the factor of beauty: that is relying too much on an elusive entity, and, also, much of the impact of art hardly is concerned with it. But the artist can fashion human creations out of nature, ranging from the orderly harmony of music and architecture to the compelling drama of the theater. Through these creations he can bring both the shock of wider experience and the satisfaction of awareness of elements that form our world. For a great work of art, the manner in which he does this has its particular quality of enjoyment and insight. The effect achieved is not a matter to lead to words about the universe, as in science or philosophy, but is a contribution to the flow of joy of existence into each person from the culture of his surroundings.

8

SCIENCE AND THE UNIVERSE

Our discussions have shown us that science both has boundless capabilities for giving us new knowledge about the world and yet is inherently limited in some important ways. As a summary, I am going to list the following salient points.

1. In science we select features of the world to be conceptually isolated, described, and related among themselves. The selection may be regarded as partially reflective of interests or needs of various kinds, and partially as an indication of what is dominant or essential in the natural world.

2. A descriptive science may be complete only in the sense that all the data sufficient to fulfill a given interest might be obtained for that part of nature which is the domain of the science.

3. There is an inherent limit to completeness in descriptive science, in that science is itself a subject for description. On the sub-atomic level, the entities to be described are themselves the medium of interaction-observation, and there are no further sub-entities or sub-quantum energies by which to obtain description of the interaction. The properties of nature *on this level* are such that it has elements of behavior which must be taken as simply given in each *individual* event, without possibility of rational, deterministic description.

4. Description of the entire universe in present-day cosmology is fragmentary and speculative. A beginning has been made, but we cannot say whether or not we shall

find the world to be that for which our physical science can attain an over-all description.

5. Scientific explanation involves the deductive structure of science, wherein individual phenomena may be seen as consequences of a general law or equation. Scientists have been highly successful in bringing many domains of the natural world into an explanatory (and predictive) scheme. But the explanation always comes to a stop with the ultimate first principles or axioms on which the deductive system is based.

6. There are many kinds of human experience, not described in science, which form part of the content of various arts.

7. The beliefs and assumptions which men hold are often traditional, but are subject to change or re-enforcement by the insights and arguments of humanists. With the extension of science to new fields, its findings often replace beliefs that had been held on grounds with less objective support. But science always operates in a context of principles that require a wider explanation or justification. A role remains, therefore, for the theologian, and for the philosopher who will consider the basic assumptions of man's thought and action.

8. The arts can bring immediate experience relating to elements of our world and ourselves in ways that science cannot, and may therefore contribute to man's perception of essential parts of the universe.

The limits to science which come from the nature of the universe are ones that can, we would expect, only be found through scientific work itself. The breakdown of ordinary space-time causal description on the atomic level is one such limit, and we might speculatively consider that another may be found in cosmology. But aside from this type of natural bound, we see that the limitations on science are of two related kinds: i) there is a lack of richness and completeness in the data of science, because of its abstraction of salient features into its descriptive framework for a domain of nature; ii) the basic principles of science do not carry an immediate conviction which makes further explanation or understanding unnecessary. These two limits are not present in direct experience, and likewise need not be present in responses of literature, art, religion, or even philosophy. In these, a much more direct, concrete experience can be conveyed than in science, and there can be an emotional content, lacking in science as such, which is its own justification, without need for explanation in its own terms. The feeling of love, the vocational call, the religious revelation, even the work of art can be convincing with no need for additional statement.

Carrying the contrast further, we might say that there are two kinds of approach to knowledge of the universe. One is the way of science, the other is the way of what I shall call awareness-emotion. This latter way, which is generally that which is transmitted through the humanities, has its extreme form in mysticism. The mystic reports a sense of both comprehension and unity with respect to the universe. Ultimately, complete knowledge of something must be a coming to be that thing, so that there is no possibility of loss of detail of knowledge in transmission. The mystic strives for just such a merging with the universe, at the same time attaining awareness or comprehension. In a much less complete way, ordinary direct experience, of the natural world or of an artist's production, gives perception of something, but with only the highly partial merging that comes with the medium of interaction: light waves, for example, if a physical object is observed, or words, if the medium is a novelist's description attempting to convey a feeling for a scene.

The extreme of science, in contrast to mysticism for the awareness-emotion approach, is the mathematical equation of high abstraction which in its consequences describes a wide range of natural phenomena. Virtually all of the immediately sensed properties of nature will have been jettisoned in the development of the equation, and its justification is hardly likely to be immediate, but rather is either by derivation from some other equation or by the validity of its consequences. The culmination of science seems to come in what we can style as a Pythagorean triumph, if we recall that Pythagoras proposed that the essential reality of the universe is to be described with numbers.

The value and truth of the approach of science are beyond question, and surely we want to continue the advance of science as man's great adventure of today. But in our time we have seen too that there has been a faltering of mankind in attainment and practice of an adequate broader set of beliefs. Clearly, the feeling-awareness approach of the humanist is not to be neglected in favor of only the scientist's approach—and indeed, it is ultimately prior to that of the scientist.

It is attractive to think of a complete philosophy that has the relevance and immediate appeal of a religion as well as the firmness and power of natural science. Is there a possibility for synthesis: can the mathematical Pythagoreanism of the scientist and the mysticism of the humanist be brought together? The present structure and content of science may hardly seem encouraging, for the direction of growth is increasingly toward abstract, deductive systems. Still, one cannot foretell the future, and we have already commented on the deep change in outlook that has come with science in the past few hundred years. This change has not been to a fixed point of view, but is a continuing process of alteration as science discloses more of the structure and process of the natural world.

I will once more cite the findings in quantum physics that bring us to a level of physical being where events as individual instances cannot be mathematically described and must be observed to be known. Here the Pythagorean move which has taken physics into the abstractions of quantum theory is abruptly checked by a necessary return to the feeling-awareness of individual observations. If natural science comes to be able to bring the domain of mind into its compass, there could well be modifications which would reduce the present apparent discontinuity between the mathematical description of an objective world and the awareness-emotion of experience. We should remember, too, that contributions can come from the humanist's side. Although I have emphasized the role of immediate experience for the humanist, it is not to be forgotten that just as such experience is also essential for the scientist, the humanist too uses rigorous thinking and perhaps can find steps toward joining with the scientist.

What we are asking for is a completion of our philosophy. At present, science tells us of an unimaginably rich and complex universe, but gives no answer to questions of meaning and significance. The traditional humanistic doctrines are, if at all, only imperfectly assimilated to science, on all levels, from everyday applications to highest theoretical generality. The manner in which science may contribute to resolving the gap is not readily foretold, but I have suggested that historically the most difficult questions in science have been answered by being asked in a new way—as in the ancient problem of the infinite divisibility of matter. We may hope that likewise new scientific knowledge is leading, for the problems of meaning and guidance of life, to a reformulation that will bring the scientist and humanist together to an adequate solution. In the meantime, we must allow science its place, but trust to the influence of the artist and the writer, to the guidance of religious and political leaders, and always to the good sense of ordinary people, in the many matters that are beyond the limits and domain of science.

INDEX

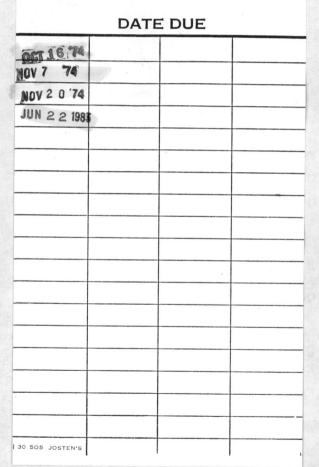

DATE DUE

OCT 16 74			
NOV 7 74			
NOV 2 0 74			
JUN 2 2 1983			
30 505 JOSTEN'S			